Donna

P9-CJH-431

Man Riding West
Louis L'Amour

Carroll & Graf Publishers, inc.
New York

FOREWORD

Louis L'Amour wrote dozens of stories for the pulps, like all striving authors, but there was something different about the characters and stories he created that made his stand out from the rest. (And that is why many readers suspected that Louis L'Amour and another contemporary pulp writer, 'Jim Mayo', were one and the same years before it was generally known).

The characters of L'Amour were not one-dimensional, nor were the stories of their lives. They were always real people, however caught up in extraordinary circumstances they might be, and, like the earlier writings of Zane Grey, they carried an aura of authenticity that made them very popular.

When Gold Medal pioneered a series of original first edition novels in paperback, they offered an opportunity for new novels to reach an immediate mass market. In 1953 they published *Hondo* by Louis L'Amour, and L'Amour began to receive widespread praise and recognition from reviewers and fans, including John Wayne and Ronald Reagan.

Louis L'Amour has become a superstar of American popular fiction, with over 100 million books in print. He is an author who has truly been a part of the Paperback Revolution, with most of his books appearing as first editions in paperback.

Carroll & Graf has been pleased to publish two first editions of Louis L'Amour stories, now in the public domain, from the early pulp magazines—*Law of the Desert Born* and *The Hills of Homicide*—and we now add two new titles, *Riding for the Brand* and *Man Riding West*, featuring more great pulp stories that have never appeared in book form before. Carroll & Graf Publishers are solely responsible for the collection and publication of these stories. We are sure that you will enjoy reading the collector's item you now hold in your hands.

The Publishers

CONTENTS

BIG MEDICINE

Old Billy Dunbar was down flat on his face in a dry wash swearing into his beard. The best gold bearing gravel he had found in a year, and then the Apaches would have to show up!

It was like them, the mean, ornery critters. He hugged the ground for dear life and hoped they would not see him, tucked away as he was between some stones where an eddy of the water that once ran through the wash had dug a trench between the stones.

There were nine of them. Not many, but enough to take his scalp if they found him, and it would be just as bad if they saw his burros or any of the prospect holes he had been sinking.

He was sweating like a stuck hog bleeds, lying there with his beard in the sand, and the old Sharps .50 ready beside him. He wouldn't have much of a chance if they found him, slithery fighters like they were, but if that old

Sharps threw down on them he'd take at least one along to the Happy Hunting Ground with him.

He could hear them now, moving along the desert above the wash. Where in tarnation were they going? He wouldn't be safe as long as they were in the country, and this was country where not many white men came. Those few who did come were just as miserable to run into as the Apaches.

There were nine of them, the leader a lean muscled man with a hawk nose. All of them slim and brown without much meat on them the way Apaches were, and wearing nothing but breech clouts and headbands.

He lay perfectly still. Old Billy was too knowing in Indian ways to start moving until he was sure they were gone. He laid right there for almost a half hour after he had last heard them, and then came out of it cautious as a bear reaching for a honey tree.

When he got on his feet, he hightailed it for the edge of the wash and took a look. The Apaches had vanished. He turned and went down the wash, taking his time and keeping the old Sharps handy. It was a mile to his burros and to the place where his prospect holes were. Luckily, he had them back in a draw where there wasn't much chance of them being found.

Billy Dunbar pulled his old gray felt hat down a little tighter and hurried on. Jennie and Julie were waiting for him, standing head to tail so they could brush flies off each other's noses.

When he got to them he gathered up his tools and took them back up the draw to the rocks at the end. His canteens were full, and he had plenty of grub and ammunition. He was lucky that he hadn't shot that rabbit when he saw it. The Apaches would have heard the

4

bellow of the Old Sharps and come for him, sure. He was going to have to be careful.

If they would just kill a man it wouldn't be so bad, but these Apaches liked to stake a man out on an ant hill and let the hot sun and ants do for him, or maybe the buzzards—if they got there soon enough.

This wash looked good, too. Not only because water had run there, but because it was actually cutting into the edge of an old river bed. If he could sink a couple of holes down to bedrock, he'd bet there'd be gold and gold aplenty.

When he awakened in the morning he took a careful look around his hiding place. One thing, the way he was located, if they caught him in camp they couldn't get at him to do much. The hollow was perhaps sixty feet across, but over half of it was covered by shelving rock from above, and the cliff ran straight up from there for an easy fifty feet. There was water in a spring and enough grass to last the burros for quite some time.

After a careful scouting around, he made a fire of dead mesquite which made almost no smoke, and fixed some coffee. When he had eaten, Dunbar gathered up his pan, his pick, shovel and rifle and moved out. He was loaded more than he liked, but it couldn't be helped.

The place he had selected to work was the inside of the little desert stream. The stream took a bend and left a gravel bank on the inside of the elbow. That gravel looked good. Putting his Sharps down within easy reach, Old Billy got busy.

Before sundown he had moved a lot of dirt, and tried several pans, loading them up and going over to the stream. Holding the pan under the water, he began to stir the gravel, breaking up the lumps of clay and stirring until every piece was wet. Then he picked out the larger stones and pebbles and threw them to one side. He put his hands on opposite sides of the pan and began to oscillate vigorously under water, moving the pan in a circular motion so the contents were shaken from side to side.

With a quick glance around to make sure there were no Apaches in sight, he tipped the pan slightly, to an angle of about 30 degrees so the lighter sands, already buoyed up by the water, could slip out over the side.

He struck the pan several good blows to help settle the gold, if any, and then dipped for more water and continued the process. He worked steadily at the pan, with occasional glances around until all the refuse had washed over the side but the heavier particles. Then with a little clean water, he washed the black sand and gold into another pan which he took from the brush where it had been concealed the day before.

For some time he worked steadily, then as the light was getting bad, he gathered up his tools, and concealing the empty pan, carried the other with him back up the wash to his hideout.

He took his Sharps and crept out of the hideout and up the wall of the canyon. The desert was still and empty on every side.

"Too empty, durn it!" he grumbled. "Them Injuns'll be back. Yuh can't fool an Apache!"

Rolling out of his blankets at sunup, he prepared a quick breakfast and then went over his takings of the day with a magnet. This black sand was mostly particles of magnetite, ilmenite, and black magnetic iron oxide. What he couldn't draw off, he next eliminated by using a blow box.

"Too slow, with them Apaches around," he grumbled. "A man workin' down there could mebbe do sixty, seventy pans a day, in that sort of gravel, but watchin' for Injuns ain't goin' t' help much!"

Yet he worked steadily, and by nightfall, despite interruptions had handled more than fifty pans. When the second day was over, he grinned at the gold he had. It was sufficient color to show he was on the right track. Right here, by using a rocker, he could have made it pay, but he wasn't looking for peanuts.

He had cached his tools along with the empty pan in the brush at the edge of the wash. When morning came, he rolled out and was just coming out of the hideout when he saw the Apache. He was squatted in the sand staring at something, and despite his efforts to keep his trail covered, Dunbar had a good idea what that something would be. He drew back into the hideout.

Lying on his middle, he watched the Indian get to his feet and start working downstream. When he got down there a little further, he was going to see those prospect holes. There would be nothing Dunbar could do then. Nor was there anything he could do now. So far as he could see, only one Apache had found him. If he fired, to kill the Indian, the others would be aware of the situation and come running.

Old Billy squinted his eyes and pondered the question. He had a hunch that Indian wasn't going to go for help. He was going to try to get Dunbar by himself, so he could take his weapons and whatever else he had of value.

The Indian went downstream further, and slipped out of sight. Billy instantly ducked out into the open and scooted down the canyon into the mesquite. He dropped flat there, and inched along in the direction the Indian had gone.

He was creeping along, getting nearer and nearer to his prospect holes, when suddenly, instinct or the subconscious hearing of a sound warned him. Like a flash, he rolled over, just in time to see the Indian leap at him, knife in hand!

Billy Dunbar was no longer a youngster, but he had lived a life in the desert, and he was hard and tough as whalebone. As the Apache leaped, he caught the knife wrist in his left hand, and stabbed at the Indian's ribs with his own knife. The Apache twisted away, and Billy gave a heave. The Indian lost balance. They rolled over, then fell over the eight foot bank into the wash!

Luck was with Billy. The Indian hit first, and Billy's knife arm was around him, with the point gouging at the Indian's back. When they landed, the knife went in to the hilt.

Billy rolled off, gasping for breath. Hurriedly, he glanced around. There was no one in sight. Swiftly, he clawed at the bank, causing the loosened gravel to cave down and in a few minutes of hot, sweating work the Indian was buried.

Turning, Billy lit out for his hideaway and when he made it, he lay there gasping for breath, his Sharps ready. There would be no work this day. He was going to lie low and watch. The other Indians would come looking, he knew.

After dark he slipped out and covered the Indian better, and then used a mesquite bush to wipe out as well as possible, the signs of their fighting. Then he catfooted it back to the hollow and tied a rawhide string across the entrance with a can of loose pebbles at the end to warn him if Indians found him. Then he went to sleep.

At dawn he was up. He checked the Sharps and then cleaned his .44 again. He loaded his pockets with cartridges just in case, and settled down for a day of it.

* * *

Luckily, he had shade. It was hot out there, plenty hot. You could fry an egg on those rocks by ten in the morning—not that he had any eggs. He hadn't even seen an egg since the last time he was in Fremont, and that had been four months ago.

He bit off a chew of tobacco and rolled it in his jaws. Then he studied the banks of the draw. An Apache could move like a ghost and look like part of the landscape. He had known them to come within fifteen feet of a man in grassy country without being seen, and no tall grass at that.

It wouldn't be so bad if his time hadn't been so short. When he left Fremont, Sally had six months to go to pay off the loan on her ranch, or out she would go. Sally's husband had been killed by a bronc down on the Sandy. She was alone with the kids and that loan about to take their home away.

When the situation became serious, Old Billy thought of this wash. Once, several years before, he had washed out some color here, and it looked rich. He had left the country about two jumps ahead of the Apaches and swore he'd never come back. Nobody else was coming out of here with gold, either, so he knew it was still like he remembered. Several optimistic prospectors had tried it, and were never heard of again. However, Old Billy had decided to take a chance. After all, Sally was all he had, and those two grandchildren of his deserved a better chance than they'd get if she lost the place.

They day moved along, a story told by the shadows on the sides of the wash. You could almost tell the time by those shadows. It wasn't long before Dunbar knew every bush, every clump of greasewood or mesquite along its length, and every rock.

He wiped the sweat from his brow and waited. Sally was a good girl. Pretty, too, too pretty to be a widow at twenty two. It was almost midafternoon when his questing eye halted suddenly on the bank of the wash. He lay perfectly still, eyes studying the bank intently. Yet his eyes had moved past the spot before they detected something amiss. He scowled, trying to remember. Then it came to him.

There had been a torn place there, as though somebody had started to pull up a clump of greasewood, then abandoned it. The earth had been exposed, and a handful of roots. Now it was blotted out. Straining his eyes he could see nothing, distinguish no contours that seemed human, only that the spot was no longer visible. The spot was mottled by shadows and sunlight through the leaves of the bush.

Then there was a movement, so slight that his eye scarcely detected it, and suddenly the earth and torn roots were visible again. They had come back. Their stealth told him they knew he was somewhere nearby, and the logical place for him would be right where he was.

Now he was in for it. Luckily, he had food, water, and ammunition. There should be just eight of them unless more had come. Probably they had found his prospect holes and trailed him back this way.

There was no way they could see into his hollow, no way they could shoot into it except through the narrow entrance which was rock and brush. There was no concealed approach to it. He dug into the bank a little to get more earth in front of himself.

No one needed to warn him of the gravity of his situation. It was one hundred and fifty miles to Fremont, and sixty miles to the nearest white man, young Sid

Barton, a cowhand turned rancher who started running some cattle on the edge of the Apache country.

Nor could he expect help. Nobody ever came into this country, and nobody knew where he was but Sally, and she only knew in a general way. Prospectors did not reveal locations where they had found color.

Well, he wasn't one of these restless young coots who'd have to be out there tangling with the Apaches. He could wait. And he would wait in the shade while they were in the sun. Night didn't worry him much. Apaches had never cared much for night fighting, and he wouldn't have much trouble with them.

One of them showed himself suddenly—only one arm and a rifle. But he fired, the bullet striking the rock overhead. Old Billy chuckled. "Tryin' t' draw fire," he said, "get me located!"

Billy Dunbar waited, grinning through his beard. There was another shot, then more stillness. He lay absolutely still. A hand showed, then a foot. He rolled his quid in his jaws and spat. An Indian suddenly showed himself, then vanished as though he had never been there. Old Billy watched the banks cynically. An Indian showed again, hesitated briefly this time, but Dunbar waited.

Suddenly, within twenty feet of the spot where Dunbar lay, an Indian slid down the bank and with a shrill whoop, darted for the entrance to the hideaway. It was point blank, even though a moving target. Billy let him have it!

The old Sharps bellowed like a stricken bull and leaped in his hands. The Apache screamed wildy and toppled over backwards, carried off his feet by the sheer force of the heavy caliber bullet. Yells of rage greeted this shot.

Dunbar could see the Indian's body sprawled under the sun. He picked up an edged piece of white stone and made a straight mark on the rock wall beside him, then seven more. He drew a diagonal line through the first one. "Seven t' go," he said.

A hail of bullets began kicking sand and dirt up around the opening. One shot hit overhead and showered dirt down almost in his face. "Durn you!" he mumbled. He took his hat off and laid it beside him, his six-shooter atop of it, ready to hand.

No more Indians showed themselves, and the day drew on. It was hot out there. In the vast brassy vault of the sky a lone buzzard wheeled.

He tried no more shots, just waiting. They were trying to tire him out. Doggone it—in this place he could outwait all the Apaches in the Southwest—not that he wanted to!

Keeping well below the bank, he got hold of a stone about the size of his head and rolled it into the entrance. Instantly, the shot smacked the dirt below it and kicked dirt into his eyes. He wiped them and swore viciously. Then he got another stone and rolled that in place, pushing dirt up behind them. He scooped his hollow deeper, and peered thoughtfully at the banks of the draw.

Jennie and Julie were eating grass, undisturbed and unworried. They had been with Old Billy too long to be disturbed by these—to them—meaningless fusses and fights. The shadow from the west bank reached farther toward the east, and Old Billy waited, watching.

He detected an almost indiscernible movement atop the bank, in the same spot where he had first seen an Indian. Taking careful aim, he drew a bead on the exposed roots and waited.

He saw no movement, yet suddenly he focused his

eyes more sharply and saw the roots were no longer exposed. Nestling the stock against his shoulder, his finger eased back on the trigger. The old Sharps wavered, and he waited. The rifle steadied, and he squeezed again.

The gun jumped suddenly and there was a shrill yell from the Apache who lunged to full height, rose on his tiptoes, both hands clasping his chest. The stricken redskin then plunged face forward down the bank in a shower of gravel. Billy reloaded and waited. The Apache lay still lying in the shadow below the bank. After watching him for a few minutes, alternating between the still form and the banks of the draw, Dunbar picked up his white stone and marked another diagonal white mark across the second straight line.

He stared at the figures with satisfaction. "Six left," he said. He was growing hungry. Jennie and Julie had both decided to lie down and call it a day.

As luck would have it, his shovel and pick were concealed in the brush at the point where the draw opened into the wider wash. He scanned the banks suddenly, and then drew back. Grasping a bush, he pulled it from the earth under the huge rocks. He then took the brush and some stones and added to his parapet. With some lumps of earth and rock he gradually built it stronger.

Always he returned to the parapet, but the Apaches were cautious and he saw nothing of them. Yet his instinct told him they were there, somewhere. And that, he knew, was the trouble. It was the fact he had been avoiding ever since he holed up for the fight. They would always be around somewhere now. Three of their braves were missing—dead. They would never let him leave the country alive.

If he had patience, so had they, and they could afford to wait. He could not. It was not merely a matter of getting home before the six month period was up—and less than two months remained of that—it was a matter of getting home with enough money to pay off the loan. And with the best of luck it would require weeks upon weeks of hard, uninterrupted work.

And then he saw the wolf.

It was no more than a glimpse, and a fleeting glimpse. Billy Dunbar saw the sharply pointed nose, and bright eyes, then the swish of a tail! The wolf vanished somewhere at the base of the shelf of rock that shaded the pocket. It vanished in proximity to the spring.

Old Billy frowned and studied the spot. He wasn't the only one holed up here! The wolf evidently had a hole somewhere in the back of the pocket, and perhaps some young, as the time of year was right. His stillness after he finished work on the entrance had evidently fooled the wolf into believing the white man was gone.

Obviously, the wolf had been lying there, waiting for him to leave so it could come out and hunt. The cubs would be getting hungry. If there were cubs.

The idea came to him then. An idea utterly fantastic, yet one that suddenly made him chuckle. It might work! It could work! At least, it was a chance, and somehow, some way, he had to be rid of those Apaches!

He knew something of their superstitions and beliefs. It was a gamble, but as suddenly as he conceived the idea, he knew it was a chance he was going to take.

Digging his change of clothes out of the saddle bags, he got into them. Then he took his own clothing and laid it out on the ground in plain sight. The pants, then the coat, the boots and nearby, the hat.

Taking some sticks he went to the entrance of the wolf

14

den and built a small fire close by. Then he hastily went back and took a quick look around. The draw was empty, but he knew the place was watched. He went back and got out of line of the wolf den, and waited.

The smoke was slight, but it was going into the den. It wouldn't take long. The wolf came out with a rush, ran to the middle of the pocket, took a quick, snarling look around and then went over the parapet and down the draw!

Working swiftly, he moved the fire and scattered the few sticks and coals in his other fireplace. Then he brushed the ground with a branch. It would be a few minutes before they moved, and perhaps longer.

Crawling into the wolf den he next got some wolf hair which he took back to his clothing. He put some of the hair in his shirt, and some near his pants. A quick look down the draw showed no sign of an Indian, but that they had seen the wolf, he knew, and he could picture their surprise and puzzlement.

Hurrying to the spring, he dug from the bank near the water a large quantity of mud. This was an added touch, but one that might help. From the mud, he formed two roughly human figures. About the head of each he tied a blade of grass.

Hurrying to the parapet for a stolen look down the draw, he worked until six such figures were made. Then, using thorns and some old porcupine quills he found near a rock, he thrust one or more through each of the mud figures.

They stood in a neat row facing the parapet. Quickly, he hurried for one last look into the draw. An Indian had emerged. He stood there in plain sight, staring toward the place!

They would be cautious, Billy knew, and he chuckled

to himself as he thought of what was to follow. Gathering up his rifle, the ammunition, a canteen and a little food, he hurried to the wolf den and crawled back inside.

On his first trip he had ascertained that there were no cubs. At the end of the den there was room to sit up, topped by the stone of the shelving rock itself. To his right, a lighted match told him there was a smaller hole of some sort.

Cautiously, Billy crawled back to the entrance, and careful to avoid the wolf tracks in the dust outside, he brushed out his own tracks, then retreated into the depths of the cave. From where he lay he could see the parapet.

Almost a half hour passed before the first head lifted above the poorly made wall. Black straight hair, a red headband, and the sharp, hard features of their leader.

Then other heads lifted beside him, and one by one the six Apaches stepped over the wall and into the pocket. They did not rush, but looked cautiously about, and their eyes were large, frightened. They looked all around, then at the clothing, then at the images. One of the Indians grunted and pointed.

They drew closer, then stopped in an awed line, staring at the mud figures. They knew too well what that meant. Those figures meant a witch doctor had put a death spell on each one of them.

One of the Indians drew back and looked at the clothing. Suddenly he gave a startled cry and pointed— at the wolf hair!

They gathered around, talking excitedly, then glancing over their shoulders fearsomely.

They had trapped what they believed to be a white man, and knowing Apaches, Old Billy would have guessed they knew his height, weight, and approximate

16

age. Those things they could tell from the length of his stride, the way he worked, the pressure of a footprint in softer ground.

They had trapped a white man, and a wolf had escaped! Now they find his clothing lying here, and on the clothing, the hair of a wolf!

All Indians knew of wolf-men, those weird creatures who changed at will from wolf to man and back again, creatures that could tear the throat from a man while he slept, and could mark his children with the wolf blood.

The day had waned, and as he lay there, Old Billy Dunbar could see that while he worked the sun had neared the horizon. The Indians looked around uneasily. This was the den of a wolf-man, a powerful spirit who had put the death spell on each of them, who came as a man and went as a wolf.

Suddenly, out on the desert, a wolf howled!

The Apaches started as if struck, and then as one man they began to draw back. By the time they reached the parapet they were hurrying.

Old Billy stayed the night in the wolf hole, lying at its mouth, waiting for dawn. He saw the wolf come back, stare about uneasily, then go away. When light came he crawled from the hole.

The burros were cropping grass and they looked at him. He started to pick up a pack saddle, then dropped it. "I'll be durned if I will!" he said.

Taking the old Sharps and the extra pan, he walked down to the wash and went to work. He kept a careful eye out, but saw no Apaches. The gold was panning out even better than he had dreamed would be possible. A few more days—suddenly, he looked up.

Two Indians stood in plain sight, facing. The nearest

17

one walked forward and placed something on a rock, then drew away. Crouched, waiting, Old Billy watched them go. Then he went to the rock. Wrapped in a piece of tanned buckskin, was a haunch of venison!

He chuckled suddenly. He was big medicine now. He was a wolf-man. The vension was a peace offering, and he would take it. He knew now he could come and pan as much gold as he liked in Apache country.

A few days later he killed a wolf, skinned it, and then buried the carcass, but of the head he made a cap to fit over the crown of his old felt hat, and wherever he went, he wore it.

A month later, walking into Fremont behind the switching tails of Jennie and Julie, he met Sally at the gate. She was talking with young Sid Barton.

"Hi," Sid said, grinning at him. Then he looked quizzically at the wolfskin cap. "Better not wear that around here! Somebody might take you for a wolf!"

"Old Billy chuckled. "I am!" he said. "Yuh're durned right, I am! Ask them Apaches!"

MAN RIDING WEST

CHAPTER ONE

The Man From Points Yonder

Three men were hunkered down by the fire when Jim Gary walked his buckskin up to their camp in the lee of the cliff. The big man across the fire had a shotgun lying beside him. It was the shotgun that made Gary uneasy, for cowhands do not carry shotguns, especially when on a trail drive as these men obviously were.

Early as it was, the cattle were already bedded down for the night in the meadow alongside the stream, and from their looks they had come far and fast. It was still light, but the clouds were low and swollen with rain.

"How's for some coffee?" Jim asked as he drew up. "I'm ridin' through, an' I'm sure hungry an' tuckered."

Somewhere off in the mountains, thunder rolled and grumbled. The fire crackled, and the leaves on the willows hung still in the lifeless air. There were three saddled horses nearby, and among the gear was an old Mother Hubbard style saddle with a wide skirt.

21

"Light an' set up," the man who spoke was lean jawed and sandy haired. "Never liked to ride on an empty stomach m'self."

More than ever, Gary felt uneasy. Neither of the others spoke. All were tough looking men, unshaven and dirty, but it was their hard-eyed suspicion that made Jim wonder. However, he swung down and loosened his saddle girth, then slipped the saddle off and laid it well back under the overhang of the cliff. As he did so he glanced again at the old saddle that lay there.

The overhang of the cliff was deep where the fire was built for shelter from the impending rain. Jim dropped to an ancient log, gray and stripped of bark, and handed his tin plate over to the man who reached for it. The cook slapped two thick slabs of beef on the plate and some frying pan bread liberally touched with the beef fryings. Gary was hungry and he dove in without comment, and the small man filled his cup.

"Headed west?" The sandy haired man asked, after a few minutes.

"Yeah, headed down below the Rim. Pleasant Valley way."

The men all turned their heads toward him but none spoke. Jim could feel their eyes on his tied down guns. There was a sheep and cattle war in the Valley.

"They call me Red Slagle. These hombres are Tobe Langer and Jeeter Dirksen. We're drivin' to Salt Creek."

Langer would be the big one. "My name's Gary," Jim replied, "Jim Gary. I'm from points yonder. Mostly Dodge an' Santa Fe."

"Hear they are hirin' warriors in Pleasant Valley."

"Reckon." Jim refused to be drawn, although he had the feeling they had warmed to him since he mentioned heading for the Valley.

"Ridin' thataway ourselves," Red suggested. "Want

to make a few dollars drivin' cattle? We're short handed."

"Might," Gary admitted, "the grub's good."

"Give you forty to drive to Salt Creek. We'll need he'p. From hereabouts the country is plumb rough an' she's fixin' to storm."

"You've hired a hand. When do I start?"

"Catch a couple of hours sleep. Tobe has the first ride. Then you take over. If you need he'p, just you call out."

Gary shook out his blankets and crawled into them. In the moment before his eyes closed he remembered the cattle had all worn a Double A brand, and the brands were fresh. That could easily be with a trail herd. But the Double A had been the spread that Mart Ray had mentioned.

It was raining when he rode out to the herd. "They ain't fussin'," Langer advised, "an' the rain's quiet enough. It should pass mighty easy. See you."

He drifted toward camp, and Gary turned up his slicker collar and studied the herd as well as he could in the darkness. They were lying quiet. He was riding a gray roped from the small remuda, and he let the horse amble placidly toward the far side of the meadow. A hundred yards beyond the meadow the bulk of the sloping hill that formed the opposite side of the valley showed blacker in the gloom. Occasionally there was a flash of heat lightning, but no thunder.

Slagle had taken him on because he needed hands, but none of them accepted him. He decided to sit tight in his saddle and see what developed. It could be plenty, for unless he was mistaken, this was a stolen herd, and Slagle was a thief, as were the others.

If this herd had come far and fast, he had come farther and faster, and with just as great a need. Now there was nothing behind him but trouble, and nothing before him but bleak years of drifting ahead of a reputation.

Up ahead was Mart Ray, and Ray was as much of a friend as he had. Gunfighters are admired by many, respected by some, feared by all and welcomed by none. His father had warned him of what to expect, warned him long ago before he himself had died in a gun battle. "You're right handy, Son," he had warned, "one of the fastest I ever seen, so don't let it be known. Don't never draw a gun on a man in anger, an' you'll live happy. Once you get the name of a gunfighter, you're on a lonesome trail, an' there's only one ending."

So he had listened, and he had avoided trouble. Mart Ray knew that. Ray was himself a gunman. He had killed six men of whom Jim Gary knew, and no doubt there had been others. He and Mart had been riding together in Texas, and then in a couple of trail drives, one all the way to Montana. He never really got close to Mart, but they had been partners, after a fashion.

Ray had always been amused at his eagerness to avoid trouble, although he had no idea of the cause of it. "Well," he had said, "they sure cain't say like father, like son. From all I hear your pappy was an uncurried wolf, an' you fight shy of trouble. You run from it. If I didn't know you so well, I'd say you was yaller."

But Mart Ray had known him well, for it had been Jim who rode his horse down in front of a stampede to pick Ray off the ground, saving his life. They got free, but no more, and a thousand head of mad cattle stampeded over the ground where Ray had stood.

Then, a month before, down in the Big Bend country, trouble had come, and it was trouble he could not avoid. It braced him in a little Mexican *cantina* just over the river, and in the person of a dark, catlike Mexican with small feet and dainty hands, but his guns were big enough and there was an unleashed devil in his eyes.

24

Jim Gary had been dancing with a Mexican girl and the Mexican had jerked her from his arms and struck her across the face. Jim knocked him down, and the Mexican got up, his eyes fiendish. Without a word, the Mexican went for his gun, and for a frozen, awful instant, Jim saw his future facing him, and then his own hand went down and he palmed his gun in a flashing, lightning draw that rapped out two shots. The Mexican, who had reached first, barely got his gun clear before he was dead. He died on his feet, then fell.

In a haze of powder smoke and anguish, Jim Gary had wheeled and strode from the door, and behind him lay dead and awful silence. It was not until two days later that he knew who and what he had killed.

The lithe bodied Mexican had been Miguel Sonoma, and he had been a legend along the Border. A tough, dangerous man with a reputation as a killer.

Two nights later, a band of outlaws from over the Border rode down upon Gary's little spread to avenge their former leader, and two of them died in the first blast of gun fire, a matter of hand guns at point blank range.

From the shelter of his cabin, Gary fought them off for three days before the smoke from his burning barn attracted help. When the help arrived, Jim Gary was a man with a name. Five dead men lay on the ground around the ranch yard and in the desert nearby. The wounded had been carried away. And the following morning, Jim turned his ranch over to the bank to sell, and lit a shuck—away from Texas.

Of this Mart Ray knew nothing. Half of Texas and all of New Mexico, or most of it, would lie behind him when he reached the banks of Salt Creek. Mart Ray was ramrodding the Double A, and he would have a job for him.

CHAPTER TWO

Ghost With The Night Herd

Jim Gary turned the horse and rode slowly back along
the side of the herd. The cattle had taken their midnight
stretch and after standing around a bit, were lying down
once more. The rain was falling, but softly, and Gary let
the gray take his own time in skirting the herd.

The night was pitch dark. Only the horns of the cattle
glistened with rain, and their bodies were a darker blob
in the blackness of the night. Once, drawing up near the
willows along the stream, Jim thought he detected a
vague sound. He waited a moment, listening. On such a
night nobody would be abroad who could help it, and it
was unlikely that a mountain lion would be on the prowl,
although possible.

He started on again, yet now his senses were alert, and
his hand slid under his slicker and touched the butt of a
.44. He was almost at the far end of the small herd when

a sudden flash of lightning revealed the hillside across the narrow valley.

Stark and clear, glistening with rain, sat a horseman! He was standing in his stirrups, and seemed amazingly tall, and in the glare of the flash, his face was stark white, like the face of a fleshless skull!

Startled, Gary grunted and slid his gun into his hand, but all was darkness again. And listen as he could, he heard no further sound. When the lightning flashed again, the hillside was empty and still. Uneasily, he caught himself staring back over his shoulder into the darkness, and he watched his horse. The gray was standing, head up and ears erect, staring off toward the darkness near the hill. Riding warily, Gary started in that direction, but when he got there, he found nothing.

It was almost daylight when he rode up to the fire which he had kept up throughout the night, and swinging down, he awakened Dirksen. The man sat up, startled. "Hey!" he exclaimed. "You forgot to call me?"

Jim grinned at him. "Just figured I was already up an' a good cook needed his sleep."

Jeeter stared at him. "You mean you rode for me? Say, you're all right!"

"Forget it!" Gary stretched. "I had a quiet night, mostly."

Red Slagle was sitting up, awakened by their talk. "What do you mean—mostly?"

Jim hesitated, feeling puzzled. "Why, to tell you the truth, I'm not sure whether I saw anything or not, but I sure thought I did. Anyway, it had me scared."

"What was it?" Slagle was pulling on his pants, but his eyes were serious. "A lion?"

"No, it was a man on a horse. A tall man with a dead white face, like a skull." Gary shrugged sheepishly.

"Makes me sound like a fool, but I figured for a moment that I'd seen a ghost!"

Red Slagle was staring at him, and Jeeter's face was dead white and his eyes were bulging. "A ghost?" he asked, faintly. "Did you say, a *ghost?*"

"Shucks," Gary shrugged, "there ain't no such thing. Just some hombre on a big black horse, passin' through in the night, that was all! But believe me, seein' him in the lightnin' up on that hill like I did, it sure was scary!"

Tobe Langer was getting up, and he too, looked bothered. Slagle came over to the fire and sat down, boots in hand. Reaching down he pulled his sock around to get a hole away from his big toe, then he put his foot into the wet boot and began to struggle with it.

"That horse now," Langer asked carefully, "did it have a white star between the eyes?"

Gary was surprised. "Why, yes! Matter of fact, it did! You know him?"

Slagle let go of the boot and stomped his foot to settle it in the boot. "Yeah, feller we seen down the road a ways. Big black horse."

Slagle and Langer walked away from camp a ways and stood talking together. Jeeter was worried. Jim could see that without half trying, and he studied the man thoughtfully. Jeeter Dirksen was a small man, quiet, but inclined to be nervous. He had neither the strength nor the toughness of Slagle and Langer. If Gary learned anything about the cattle it would be through his own investigation or from Jeeter. And he was growing more and more curious.

Yet, if these were Double A cattle, and had been stolen, why were they being driven toward the AA ranch, rather than away from it? He realized suddenly that he knew nothing at all about Red Slagle nor his outfit, and it was time he made some inquiries.

"This Double A," he asked suddenly, "you been ridin' for them long?"

Dirksen glanced at him sharply, and bent over his fire. "Not long," he said. "It's a Salt Creek outfit. Slagle's segundo."

"Believe I know your foreman," Gary suggested, "I think this was the outfit he said. Hombre name of Mart Ray. Ever hear of him?"

Jeeter turned sharply, slopping coffee over the rim of the cup. It hissed in the fire, and both men looked around at the camp. Jeeter handed the cup to Gary and studied him, searching his face. Then he admitted cautiously, "Yeah, Ray's the foreman. Ranch belongs to a syndicate out on the coast. You say you know him?"

"Uh huh. Used to ride with him." Langer and Slagle had walked back to the fire, and Dirksen poured coffee for them.

"Who was that you rode with?" Slagle asked.

"Your boss, Mart Ray."

Both men looked up sharply, then Slagle's face cleared and he smiled. "Say! That's why the name was familiar! You're *that* Jim Gary! Son of Old Steve Gary. Yeah, Mart told us about you."

Langer chuckled suddenly. "You're the scary one, huh? The one who likes to keep out of trouble. Yeah, we heard about you!"

The contempt in his tone stiffened Jim's back, and for an instant he was on the verge of a harsh retort, then the memory of what lay behind him welled up within, and bitterly he kept his mouth shut. If he got on the prod and killed a man here, he would only have to drift farther. There was only one solution, and that was to avoid

29

trouble. Yet irritating as it was to be considered lacking in courage, Langer's remark let him know that the story of his fights had not preceded him.

"There's no call," he said, after a minute, "to go around the country killin' folks. If people would just get the idea they can get along without all that. Me, I don't believe in fightin'."

Langer chuckled, but Slagle said nothing, and Dirksen glanced at him sympathetically.

All day the herd moved steadily west, but now Gary noticed a change, for the others were growing more watchful as the day progressed, and their eyes continued to search the surrounding hills, and they rode more warily approaching any bit of cover.

Once, when Jeeter rode near him, the little man glanced across the herd at the other riders, then said quietly, "That was no ghost you saw. Red rode up there on the hill, an' there was tracks, tracks of a mighty big black horse."

"Wonder why he didn't ride down to camp?" Jim speculated. "He sure enough saw the fire!"

Dirksen grunted. "If that hombre was the one Red thinks it is, he sure didn't have no aim to ride down there!"

Before Gary could question him further, Jeeter rode off after a stray and cutting him back into the herd, rode on further ahead. Jim dropped back to the drag, puzzled over this new angle. Who could the strange rider be? What did he want? Was he afraid of Slagle?

A big brindle steer was cutting wide of the herd and Jim swung out to get him, but dashing toward the stream, the steer floundered into the water and into quicksand. Almost at once, it was down, struggling madly, its eyes rolling.

Jim swung a loop and dropped it over the steers horns. If he could give the steer a little help now there was a chance he could get it out before it bogged in too deep.

He started the buckskin back toward more solid ground and with the pull on the rope and the struggling of the steer, he soon had it out on the bank of the stream. The weary animal stumbled and went down, and shaking his loop loose, Gary swung his horse around to get the animal up. Something he saw on the flank made him swing down beside the steer. Curiously, he bent over the brand.

It had been worked over! The Double A had been burned on over a Slash Four!

"Somethin' wrong?"

The voice was cold and level, and Jim Gary started guiltily, turning. Then his eyes widened. "Mart! Well, for cryin' out in the night time! Am I glad to see *you!*"

Ray stared. "For the luvva Pete, if it ain't Gary! Say, how did you get here? Don't tell me you're drivin' that herd up ahead?"

"That's right! Your outfit, ain't it? I hired on back down the line. This steer just got hisself bogged down an' I had a heck of a time gettin' him out. You seen Red an' the boys?"

"Not yet. I swung wide. Get that steer on his feet an' we'll join 'em."

Yet as they rode back, despite Ray's affability, Gary was disturbed. Something here was very wrong. This was a Slash Four steer with the brand worked over to a Double A, the brand for which Ray was foreman. If these cattle were rustled, then Mart Ray was party to it, and so were Slagle, Langer and Dirksen! And, if caught with these men and cattle, so was he!

He replied to Ray's questions as well as he could, and briefly, aware that his friend was preoccupied and thinking of something else. Yet at the same time he was pleased that Ray asked him no questions about his reasons for leaving home.

Mart Ray rode up ahead and joined Slagle and he could see the two men riding on together, deep in conversation. When they bedded down for the night there had been no further chance to talk to him, and Gary was just as well satisfied, for there was much about this that he did not like. Nor was anything said about the midnight rider. When day broke, Mart Ray was gone. "Rode on to Salt Creek," Red said, "we'll see him there." He glanced at Jim, his eyes amused. "He said to keep you on, that you was a top-hand."

Despite the compliment, Jim was nettled. What else had Ray told Slagle? His eyes narrowed. Whatever it was, he was not staying on. He was going to get shut of this outfit just as fast as he could. All he wanted was his time. Yet by midday he had not brought himself to ask for it.

Dirksen had grown increasingly silent, and he avoided Langer and Slagle. Watching him, Jim was puzzled by the man, but could find no reason for his behavior unless the man was frightened by something. Finally, Jim pulled up alongside Jeeter.

The man glanced at him, and shook his head. "I don't like this. Not even a little. She's too quiet."

Gary hesitated, waiting for the cowhand to continue, but he held his peace. Finally, Gary said, speaking slowly, "It is mighty quiet, but I see nothin' wrong with that. I'm not hunting trouble."

"Trouble," Jeeter said dryly, "comes sometimes whether you hunt it or not. If anything breaks around this herd, take my advice an' don't ask no questions. Just scatter dust out of here!"

"Why are you warning me?" Gary asked.

Jeeter shrugged. "You seem like a right nice feller," he said quietly. "Shame for you to get rung in on somethin' as dirty as this when you had nothin' to do with it."

CHAPTER THREE

Boss of the Slash Four

Despite his questions, Jeeter would say no more, and finally Gary dropped back to the drag. There was little dust, due to the rains, but the drag was a rough deal for the herd was tired and they kept lagging back. Langer and Slagle, Jim observed, spent more time watching the hills than the cattle. Obviously, both men were as jumpy as Dirksen, and were expecting something. Toward dust Red left the herd and rode up a canyon into the hills.

Slagle was still gone, and Jim was squatting by the fire watching Jeeter throw grub together when there was a sudden shot from the hills to the north.

Langer stopped his nervous pacing and faced the direction of the shot, his hand on his gun. Jim Gary got slowly to his feet, and he saw that Jeeter's knuckles gripping the frying pan were white and hard.

Langer was first to relax. "Red must have got him a

turkey," he said, "few around here, and he was sayin' earlier he'd sure like some."

Nevertheless, Gary noted that Langer kept back from the firelight and had his rifle near at hand. There was a sound of an approaching horse and Langer slid his rifle across his knees, but it was Slagle, and he swung down, glancing toward the big man. "Shot at a turkey, an' missed." Then he added, looking right at Langer, "Nothin' to worry about now. This time for sure."

Dirksen got suddenly to his feet. "I'm quittin', Red. I don't like this a-tall, not none. I'm gettin' out."

Slagle's eyes were flat and ugly. "Sit down an' shut up, Jeeter," he said impatiently, "tomorrow's our last day. We'll have a payday this side of Salt Creek an' then if you want to blow, why you can blow out of here."

Gary looked up. "I reckon you can have my time, then, too," he said quietly, "I'm ridin' west for Pleasant Valley."

"You?" Langer snorted. "Pleasant Valley? You better stay somewhere where you can be took care of. They don't side-step trouble out there."

Gray felt something rise within him, but he controlled his anger with an effort. "I didn't ask you for any comment, Tobe," he said quietly, "I can take care of myself."

Langer sneered. "Why, you yaller skunk! I heard all about you! Just because your pappy was a fast man, you must think folks are skeered of you! You're yaller as saffron! You ain't duckin' trouble, you're just scared!"

Gary was on his feet, his face white. "All you've got to do, Tobe, if you want to lose some teeth, is to stand up!"

"*What?*" Langer leaped to his feet. "Why, you dirty—"

Jim Gary threw a roundhouse left. The punch was

35

wide, but it came fast, and Langer was not expecting Jim to fight. Too late, he tried to duck, but the fist caught him on the nose, smashing it and showering the front of his shirt with gore.

The big man was tough, and he sprang in, swinging with both hands. Gary stood his ground, and began to fire punches with both fists. For a full minute the two big men stood toe to toe and slugged wickedly, and then Gary deliberately gave ground. Over eager, Langer leaped after him, and Gary brought up a wicked right that stood Tobe on his boot toes, then a looping left that knocked him into the fire.

With a cry, he leaped from the flames, his shirt smoking. Ruthlessly, Gary grabbed him by the shirt front and jerked him into a right hand to the stomach, then a right to the head, and shoving him away he split his ear with another looping left, smashing it like an over ripe tomato. Langer went down in a heap.

Red Slagle had made no move to interfere, but his eyes were hard and curious as he stared up at Gary. "Now where," he said, "did Ray get the idea that you wouldn't fight?"

Gary spilled water from a canteen over his bloody knuckles. "Maybe he just figured wrong. Some folks don't like trouble. That don't mean they won't fight when they have to."

Langer pulled himself drunkenly to his feet and staggered toward the creek.

Red measured Jim with careful eyes. "What would you do," he asked suddenly, "if Langer reached for a gun?"

Gary turned his level green eyes toward Slagle. "Why, I reckon I'd have to kill him," he said, matter-of-factly. "I hope he ain't so foolish."

Dawn broke cold and gray and Jim Gary walked his horse up into the hills where he had heard the shot the night before. He knew that if Slagle saw him, he would be in trouble, but there was much he wanted to know.

Despite the light fall of rain the night before, there were still tracks. He followed those of Slagle's bay until he found where they joined those of a larger horse. Walking the buckskin warily, Jim followed the trail. It came to a sudden end.

A horse was sprawled in a clearing, shot through the head. A dozen feet away lay an old man, a tall old man, his sightless eyes staring toward the lowering skies, his arms flung wide. Jim bent over him and saw that he had been shot three times through the chest. Three times. And the wound lower down was an older wound, several days old at least.

The horse wore a Slash Four brand. Things were beginning to make sense now. Going through the old man's pockets. Jim found a worn envelope containing some tallies of cattle, and the envelope was addressed to *Tom Blaze, Durango, Colo.*

Tom Blaze . . . the Slash Four!

Tom Blaze, the pioneer Kiowa fighting cattleman who owned the Slash Four, one of the toughest outfits in the West! Why he had not connected the two Jim could not imagine, but the fact remained that the Slash Four had struck no responsive chord in his thoughts until now.

And Tom Blaze was dead.

Now it all fitted. The old Mother Hubbard saddle had been taken from Tom's horse, for this was the second time he had been shot. Earlier, perhaps when the cattle had been stolen, they had shot him and left him for dead, yet they had been unable to leave the saddle behind, for a saddle was two or three month's work for a cowhand, and not to be lightly left behind.

They had been sure of themselves, too. Sure until he saw Blaze, following them despite his wound. After that they had been worried, and Slagle must have sighted Blaze the afternoon before, then followed him and shot him down.

When the Slash Four found Tom Blaze dead all heck would break loose. Dirksen knew that, and that was why he wanted out, but fast. And it was why Red Slagle and Tobe Langer had pushed so hard to get the cattle to Salt Creek where they could be lost in larger herds, or in the breaks of the hills around the Double A.

When he rode the buckskin down to the fire the others were all up and moving around. Langer's face was swollen and there were two deep cuts, one on his cheekbone, the other over an eye. He was sullen and refused to look toward Gary.

Slagle stared at the buckskin suspiciously, noticing the wetness on his legs from riding in the high grass and brush.

Whatever the segundo had in mind he never got a chance to say. Jim Gary poured a cup of coffee, but held it in his left hand. "Red, I want my money. I'm takin' out."

"Mind if I ask why?" Red's eyes were level and waiting.

Gary knew that Slagle was a gun hand but the thought did not disturb him. While he avoided trouble, it was never in him to be afraid, nor did his own skill permit it. While he had matched gun speed with only one man, he had that sure confidence that comes from unerring marksmanship and speed developed from long practice.

"No, I don't mind. This morning I found Tom Blaze's body, right where you killed him yesterday afternoon. I know that Slash Four outfit, and I don't want to be any part of this bunch when they catch up to you."

His frankness left Slagle uncertain. He had been prepared for evasion. This was not only sincerity, but it left Slagle unsure as to Gary's actual stand. From his words Slagle assumed Gary was leaving from dislike of the fight rather than dislike of rustling.

"You stick with us, Jim," he said, "you're a good man, like Mart said. That Slash Four outfit won't get wise, and there'll be a nice split on this cattle deal."

"I want no part of it," Jim replied shortly. "I'm out. Let me have my money."

"I ain't got it," Red said simply. "Ray pays us all off. I carry no money around. Come on, Jim, lend us a hand. We've only today, then we'll be at the head of Salt Creek Wash and get paid off."

Gary hesitated. He did need the money, for he was broke and would need grub before he could go on west. Since he had come this far, another day would scarcely matter. "All right, I'll finish the drive."

Nothing more was said, and within the hour they moved out. Yet Gary was restless and worried. He could feel the tenseness in the others and knew they, too, were disturbed. There was no sign of Mart Ray, who should be meeting them soon.

To make matters worse, the cattle were growing restive. The short drives had given them time to recover some of their energy and several of them, led by one big red steer, kept breaking for the brush. It was hot, miserable work. The clouds still hung low, threatening rain, but the air was sultry.

Jim Gary started the day with the lean gray horse he

had ridden before, but by midafternoon he exchanged the worn out animal for his own buckskin. Sweat streamed down his body under his shirt, and he worked hard, harrying the irritable animals down the trail that now was lined with piñon and juniper, with a sprinkling of huge boulders. Ahead, a wide canyon opened, and not far beyond would be the spot where he expected to find Ray with the payoff money.

The big red steer suddenly made another bolt for the brush and the buckskin unwound so fast that it almost unseated Gary. He swore softly and let the horse take him after the steer and cut it back to the herd. As it swung back, he glanced up to see Langer and Red Slagle vanishing into the brush. Where Dirksen was he could not guess until he heard a wild yell.

Swinging around, he saw a dozen hard riding horsemen cutting down from the brush on both sides, and a glance told him that flight was useless. Nevertheless, Jeeter Dirksen tried it.

Slamming the spurs into his bronc, he lunged for the brush in the direction taken by Slagle and Langer, but he made no more than a dozen yards when a rattle of gunfire smashed him from the saddle. His slender body hit the ground rolling, flopped over one last time, and lay sprawled and sightless under the low gray clouds.

Gary rested his hands on his saddlehorn and stared gloomily at the strange little man, so badly miscast in this outlaw venture. Then horsemen closed in around him; his six-guns were jerked from their holsters, and his rifle from its scabbard.

"What's the matter with you?" The voice was harsh. "Won't that horse of yours run?"

Jim looked up into a pair of cold gray eyes in a

leatherlike face. A neat gray mustache showed above a firm lipped mouth. Jim Gary smiled, although he had never felt less like it in his life. The horsemen surrounded him, and their guns were ready. "Never was much of a hand to run," Jim said, "an' I've done nothin' to run for."

"You call murderin' my brother nothin'? You call stealin' cattle nothin'? Sorry, friend, we don't see things things alike. I call it hangin'."

"So would I, on'y I haven't done those things. I hired onto this oufit back down the line. Forty bucks to the head of Salt Creek Wash . . . an' they ain't paid me."

"You'll get paid!" The speaker was a lean, hard faced young man. "With a rope!"

Another ride pushed a horse through the circle. "Who is this man, Uncle Dan? Why didn't he try to get away?"

"Says he's just a hired hand," Uncle Dan commented.

"That's probably what that dead man would have said, too!" the lean puncher said. "Let me an' the boys have him under that cottonwood we seen. It had nice strong limbs."

Gary had turned his head to look at the girl. Uncle Dan would be Dan Blaze, and this must be the daughter of the murdered man. She was tall, slim but rounded of limb and undeniably attractive, with color in her cheeks and a few scattered freckles over her nose. Her eyes were hazel and now looked hard and stormy.

"Did you folks find Tom Blaze's body?" he asked. "They left him back yonder." Lifting a hand carefully to his shirt pocket he drew out the envelope and tally sheets. "These were his."

"What more do you need?" The lean puncher demanded. He pushed his horse against Jim's and grabbed at the buckskin's bridle. "Come on, boys!"

"Take it easy, Jerry!" Dan Blaze said sharply. "When I want him hung, I'll say so." His eyes shifted back to Jim. "You're a mighty cool customer," he said. "If your story's straight, what are you doing with these?"

Briefly as possible, Jim explained the whole situation, and ended by saying, "What could I do? I still had forty bucks comin', an' I did my work, so I aim to collect."

"You say there were three men with the herd? And the two who got away were Tobe Langer and Red Slagle?"

"That's right," Jim hesitated over Mart Ray, then said no more.

Blaze was staring at the herd, now he looked at Jim. "Why were these cattle branded AA? That's a straight outfit. You know anything about that?"

Gary hesitated. Much as he had reason to believe Ray was not only one of these men but their leader, he hated to betray him. "Not much. I don't know any of these outfits. I'm a Texas man."

Blaze smiled wryly. "You sound it. What's your handle?"

"Jim Gary."

The puncher named Jerry started as if struck. "Jim Gary?" he gasped, his voice incredulous. "The one who killed Sonoma?"

"Yeah, I reckon."

Now they were all staring at him with new interest, for the two fights he had were ample to start his name growing a legend on the plains and desert. These punchers had heard of him, probably from some grub line rider or drifting puncher.

"Jim Gary," Blaze mused, "we've heard about you. Old Steve's son, aren't you? I knew Steve."

Jim looked up his eyes cold. "My father," he said grimly, "was a mighty good man!"

42

Dan Blaze's eyes warmed a little. "You're right. He was."

"What of it?" Jerry demanded sullenly. "The man's a killer. We know that. We found him with the cattle. We found him with some of Tom's stuff on him. What more do you want?"

The girl spoke suddenly. "There was another rider, one who joined you, then rode away. Who was he?"

There it was, and Jim suddenly knew he would not lie. "Mart Ray," he said quietly, "of the Double A."

"That's a lie!" The girl flashed back. "What are you saying?"

"You got any proof of that?" Jerry demanded hotly. "You're talkin' about a friend of our'n."

"He was a friend of mine, too." Gary explained about Mart Ray. "Why don't you turn me loose?" he suggested then. "I'll go get Ray and bring him to you. Chances are Slagle and Tobe will be with him."

"You'll get him?" Jerry snorted. "That's a good one, that is!"

"Tie him," Dan Blaze said suddenly. "We'll go into Salt Creek."

CHAPTER FOUR

Hoofmarked For Justice

Riding behind Dan Blaze and his niece, whom he heard them call Kitty, Jim Gary was suddenly aware, almost for the first time, of the danger he was in. The fact that it had been averted for the moment was small consolation, for these were hard, desperate men, and one of them, perhaps more, had been slain.

Fear was something strange to him, and while he had known danger, it had passed over him leaving him almost untouched. This situation conveyed only a sense of unreality, and until now the idea that he might really be in danger scarcely seemed credible. Listening to these men, his mind changed about that. He realized belatedly that he was in the greatest danger of his life. If he had none of their talk to warn him, the mute evidence of Jeeter's body was enough. And Jeeter had died yelling to him, trying to give him a warning so he might escape.

Now fear rode with him, a cold, clammy fear that

44

stiffened his fingers and left his mouth dry and his stomach empty. Even the sight of the scattered buildings of the town of Salt Creek did not help, and when they rode up the street, the red of emabarrassment crept up his neck at the shame of being led into the town, his hands tied behind him, like a cheap rustler.

Mart Ray was sitting on the steps and he shoved his hat back and got to his feet. Beside him was Red Slagle. There was no sign of Tobe Langer. "Howdy, Dan! What did you catch? A hoss thief?" Ray's voice was genial, his eyes bland. "Looks like a big party for such a small catch!"

Blaze reined in his horse and stopped the little cavalcade. His eyes went from Mart to Slagle. "How long have you been here, Red?" he demanded.

"Me?" Slagle was innocent. "No more'n about fifteen minutes, maybe twenty. Just rode in from the Double A. Somethin' wrong?"

Blaze turned his cold eyes on Jim Gary, then looked back to Ray. "We found a herd of Slash Four cattle east of here, Mart. They were wearin' a Double A brand worked over our Slash Four. How do you explain it?"

Ray shrugged. "I don't," he said simply. "How does that hombre you got with you explain it?"

Kitty Blaze spoke up quickly. "Mart, did you ever see this man before? Did you?"

Ray stared at Gary. "Not that I recall," he said seriously. "He sure don't look familiar to me!"

"Blaze," Gary said suddenly, "if you'll turn my hands loose and give me a gun I can settle this in three minutes! I can prove he's a liar! I can prove that he does know me, an' that I know him!"

"There's nothin' you can prove with a gun you can't prove without it!" Blaze said flatly. "Whatever you

45

know, spill it! Else you're gettin' your neck stretched! I'm tired of this fussin' around!"

Jim Gary kneed his horse foreward. His eyes were hot and angry. "Mart," he said, "I always suspected there was a streak of coyote in you, but I never knowed you'd be this low down. I don't like to remind anybody of what I done for him, but I recall a stampede I hauled you out of. Are you goin' to talk?"

Ray shook his head smiling. "This is a lot of trouble, Dan. Take him away and stretch his neck before I get sore and plug him."

"You'd be afraid to meet me with a gun, Mart. You always were afraid!" Jim taunted. "That's why you left Red and Tobe with the cattle. You wanted the profit but none of the trouble! Well, you've got trouble now! If I had a gun I'd see you eat dirt!"

Mart Ray's face was ugly. "Shut up, you fool! You call me yellow? Why, everybody knows you're yellow as—!" He caught himself abruptly, his face paling under the tan.

"What was that, Ray?" Dan Blaze's face had sharpened. "Ever'body knows what about him? If you've never seen him before, how could you say ever'body calls him yellow?"

Ray shrugged. "Just talkin' too fast, that's all!" He turned and stepped up on the sidewalk. "He's your man. You settle your own war." Ray turned to go, but Jim yelled at him, and Ray wheeled.

"Mart, if I don't know you, how do I know you've got a white scar down your right side, a scar made by a steer's hoof?"

Ray laughed, but it was a strained laugh. He looked trapped now, and he took an involuntary step backward. "That's silly!" he scoffed. "I've no such scar!"

46

"Why not take off your shirt?" Jerry said suddenly. "That will only take a minute." The lean jawed cowhand's face was suddenly hard. "I think I remember you having such a scar, from one time I seen you swimmin' in the San Juan. Take off your shirt an' let's see!"

Mart Ray backed up another step, his face sharp and cold. "I'll be damned if I take off my shirt in the street for any low down rustler!" he snapped. "This here nonsense has gone far enough!"

"Loose my hands!" Jim pleaded in a whisper. "I'll take his shirt off!"

Kitty stared at him. Her face was white and strained, but in her eyes he now saw a shadow of doubt. Yet it was Jerry who acted suddenly, and jerked him around and before anyone realized what he had done, he severed the bonds with a razor sharp knife and jerked the ropes from his hands. With almost the same gesture, he slammed guns in Gary's holsters. "All right! Maybe I'm crazy!" he snapped. "But go to it!"

The whole action had taken less than a minute, and Mart Ray had turned his back and started away while Blaze waited in indecision. It was Red Slagle who saw Jim Gary hit the ground. "Boss!" he yelled. His voice was suddenly sharp with panic. "Look out!"

Ray wheeled, and when he saw Gary coming toward him, chafing his wrists, he stood still, momentarily dumbfounded. Then he laughed. "All right, Yellow! You're askin' for it! This is one bunch of trouble you can't duck! You've ducked your last fight!"

Furious, he failed to realize the import of his words, and he dropped into a half crouch, his hands ready above his gun butts. It was Jerry who shook him. Jerry who

47

made the casual remark that jerked Mart Ray to realization of what he was facing.

"Looks like whatever Ray knows about him, he sure ain't heard about Jim Gary killin' Miguel Sonoma!"

Mart Ray was staggered. "Sonoma?" he gasped. "You killed Sonoma?"

Jim Gary was facing him now. Some of the numbness was gone from his hands, and something cold and terrible was welling up within him. He had ridden beside this man, shared food with him, worked with him, and now the man had tricked and betrayed him.

"Yes, Mart, I killed Sonoma. I ain't afraid. I never was. I just don't like trouble!"

Ray's tongue touched his lips and his eyes narrowed to slits, he sank a little deeper into the crouch, and men drew away to the sides of the street. Scarcely twenty feet apart, the two faced each other. "Take off your shirt, Ray. Take it off and show them. Reach up slow and unbutton it. You take it off yourself, or I'll take it off your body!"

"Go to blazes!" Ray's voice was hoarse and strange. Then, with incredible swiftness, his hands dropped for the guns.

In the hot, dusty stillness of the afternoon street, all was deathly still. Somewhere a baby cried, and a foot shifted on the board walk. For what seemed an age, all movement seemed frozen and still as the two men in the street faced each other.

Kitty Blaze, her eyes wide with horror, seemed caught in that same breathless, time frozen hush. The hands of the men were moving with flashing speed, but at that instant everything seemed to move hauntingly slow. She saw

Mart Ray's gun swing up, she saw the killing eagerness in his face, his lips thinned and white, his eyes blazing.

And she saw the stranger, Jim Gary. Tall, lithe and strong, his dark face passionless, yet somehow ruthless. And she saw his lean brown hand flash in a blur of movement, saw flame leap from the black muzzles of his guns, and saw Mart Ray smashed back, back, back! She saw his body flung sideways into the hitching rail, saw a horse rear, his lashing hoofs within inches of the man, she saw the gun blaze again from the ground, and a leap of dust from the stranger's shoulder, and she saw Gary move coolly aside to bring his guns better to bear upon the man who was now struggling up.

As in a kind of daze, she saw Jim Gary holding his fire, letting Ray get to his feet. In that stark, incredible instant, she saw him move his lips and she heard the words, as they all heard them in the silence of the street. "I'm sorry, Mart. You shouldn't have played it this way. I'd rather it had been the stampede."

And then Ray's guns swung up. His shirt was bloody, his face twisted in a sort of leer torn into his cheek by a bullet, but his eyes were fiendish. The guns came up, and even as they came level, red flame stabbed from the muzzle of Gary's guns and Ray's body jerked, dust sprang from his shirt's back, and he staggered back, sat down on the edge of the walk, and then as though taken with a severe pain in the groin, he rolled over into the street and sprawled out flat. Somewhere thunder rolled.

For a long moment, the street was motionless. Then somebody said, "We better get inside. She's rainin'."

Jerry swung from his horse and in a couple of strides was beside the fallen man. Ripping back the shirt, he exposed the side, scarred by a steer's hoof.

Dan Blaze jerked around. "Slagle!" he yelled. "Where's Red Slagle! Get him!"

"Here." Slagle was sitting against the building, gripping a bloody hand. "I caught a slug. I got behind Ray." He looked up at Blaze. "Gary's right. He's straight as a string. It was Ray's idea to ring him in and use him as the goat after he found him with us."

Dan Blaze knelt beside him. "Who killed my brother?" he demanded. "Was it you or Ray?"

"Ray shot him first. I finished it. I went huntin' for him an' he busted out of the brush. He had a stick he'd carried for walkin' an' I mistook it for a gun."

"What about Langer?" Gary demanded. "Where's he?"

Red grinned, a hard, cold grin. "He lit a shuck. That whuppin' you gave him took somethin' out of him. Once he started to run he didn't stop, not even for his money."

He dug into his pocket. "That reminds me. Here's the forty bucks you earned."

Jim Gary took the money, surprised speechless. Slagle struggled erect. Gary's expression seemed to irritate him. "Well, you earned it didn't you? An' I hired you, didn't I? Well, I never gypped no man out of honest wages yet!

"Anyway," he added wryly, "by the looks of that rope I don't reckon I'll need it. Luck to you, kid! An'," he grinned, "stay out of trouble!"

Thunder rumbled again, and rain poured into the street, a driving, pounding rain that would start the washes running and bring the grass to life again, green and waving for the grazing cattle, moving west, moving north.

HIS BROTHER'S
DEBT

"You're yellow, Casady!" Ben Kerr shouted. "Yellow as saffron! You ain't got the guts of a coyote! Draw, curse you, fill your hand so I can kill you! You ain't fit to live!" Kerr stepped forward, his big hands spread over his gun butts. "Go ahead, *reach!*"

Rock Casady, numb with fear, stepped slowly back, his face gray. To right and left were the amazed and incredulous faces of his friends, the men he had ridden with on the O Bar, staring unbelieving.

Sweat broke out on his face. He felt his stomach retch and twist within him. Turning suddenly, he plunged blindly through the door and fled.

Behind him, one by one, his shame-faced, unbelieving friends from the O Bar slowly sifted from the crowd. Heads hanging, they headed homeward. Rock Casady was yellow. The man they had worked with, sweated with, laughed with. The last man they would have suspected. Yellow.

Westward, with the wind in his face and tears burning his eyes, his horse's hoofs beating out a mad tattoo upon the hard trail, fled Rock Casady, alone in the darkness.

Nor did he stop. Avoiding towns and holding to the hills, he rode steadily westward. There were days when he starved, and days when he found game, a quail or two, killed with unerring shots from a six-gun that never seemed to miss. Once he shot a deer. He rode wide of towns and deliberately erased his trail, although he knew no one was following him, or cared where he went.

Four months later, leaner, unshaven and saddle weary, he rode into the yard of the Three Spoke Wheel. Foreman Tom Bell saw him coming and glanced around at his boss, big Frank Stockman.

"Look what's comin'. Looks like he's lived in the hills. On the dodge, maybe."

"Huntin' grub, most likely. He's a strappin' big man, though, an' looks like a hand. Better ask him if he wants a job. With Pete Vorys around, we'll have to be huntin' strangers or we'll be out of help!"

The mirror on the wall of the bunkhouse was neither cracked nor marred, but Rock Casady could almost wish that it was. Bathed and shaved, he looked into tortured eyes of a dark, attractive young man with wavy hair and a strong jaw.

People had told him many times that he was a handsome man, but when he looked into his eyes he knew he looked into the eys of a coward.

He had a yellow streak.

The first time—well, the first time but one—that he had faced a man with a gun he had backed down cold. He had run like a baby. He had shown the white feather.

54

Tall, strongly built, skillful with rope or horse, knowing with stock, he was a top hand in any outfit. An outright genius with guns, men had often said they would hate to face him in a shoot-out. He had worked hard and played rough, getting the most out of life until that day in the saloon in El Paso when Ben Kerr, gunman and cattle rustler, gambler and bully, had called him, and he had backed down.

Tom Bell was a knowing and kindly man. Aware that something was riding Casady, he told him his job and left him alone. Stockman watched him top off a bad bronc on the first morning and glanced at Bell.

"If he does everything like he rides, we've got us a hand!"

And Casady did everything as well. A week after he had hired out he was doing as much work as any two men. And the jobs they avoided, the lonely jobs, he accepted eagerly.

"Notice something else?" Stockman asked the ranch owner one morning. "That new hand sure likes jobs that keep him away from the ranch."

Stockman nodded. "Away from people. It ain't natural, Tom. He ain't been to Three Lakes once since he's been here."

Sue Landon looked up at her uncle. "Maybe he's broke!" she exclaimed. "No cowhand could have fun in town when he's broke!"

Bell shook head. "It ain't that, Sue. He had money when he first came in here. I saw it. He had anyway two hundred dollars and for a forty-a-month cowpoke, that's a lot of money!"

"Notice something else?" Stockman asked. "He never packs a gun. Only man on the ranch who doesn't. You'd better warn him about Pete Vorys."

"I did," Bell frowned. "I can't figure this hombre, boss. I did warn him, and that was the very day he began askin' for all the bad jobs. Why, he's the only man on the place who'll fetch grub to Cat McLeod without bein' bullied into it!"

"Over in that Rock Canyon country?" Stockman smiled. "That's a rough ride for any man. I don't blame the boys, but you've got to hand it to old Cat. He's killed nine lions and forty-two coyotes in the past ninety days! If he keeps that up we won't have so much stock lost!"

"Two bad he ain't just as good on rustlers. Maybe," Bell grinned, "we ought to turn him loose on Pete Vorys!"

Rock Casady kept his palouse gelding moving steadily. The two pack horses ambled placidly behind, seemingly content to be away from the ranch. The old restlessness was coming back to Casady, and he had been on the Three Spoke only a few weeks. He knew they liked him, knew that despite his taciturn manner and desire to be alone, the hands liked him as well as did Stockman or Bell.

He did his work and more and he was a hand. He avoided poker games that might lead to trouble and stayed away from town. He was anxiously figuring some way to be absent from the ranch on the following Saturday, for he knew the whole crowd was going to a dance and shindig in Three Lakes.

While he talked little, he heard much. He was aware of impending trouble between the Three Spoke Wheel outfit and the gang of Pete Vorys. The latter, who seemed to ride the country as he pleased, owned a small ranch north of Three Lakes, near town. He had a dozen tough hands and usually spent money freely. All his hands had money, and while no one dared say it, all knew he was rustling.

Yet he was not the ringleader. Behind him there was someone else, someone who had only recently become involved, for recently there had been a change. Larger bunches of cattle were being stolen, and more care was taken to leave no trail. The carelessness of Vorys had given way to more shrewd operation, and Casady overheard enough talk to know that Stockman believed a new brain was directing operations.

He heard much of Pete Vorys. He was a big man, bigger than Rock. He was a killer with at least seven notches on his gun. He was pugnacious and quarrelsome, itching for a fight with gun or fists. He had, only a few weeks ago, whipped Sandy Kane, a Three Spoke hand, within an inch of his life. He was bold, domineering, and tough.

The hands on the Three Spoke were good men. They were hard workers, willing to fight, but not one of them was good enough to tackle Vorys with either fists or gun.

Cat McLeod was scraping a hide when Rock rode into his camp in Blue Spring Valley. He got up, wiping his hands on his jeans and grinning.

"Howdy, son! You sure are a sight for sore eyes! It ain't no use quibblin', I sure get my grub on time when you're on that ranch! Hope you stay!"

Rock swung down. He liked the valley and liked Cat.

"Maybe I'll pull out, Cat." He looked around. "I might even come up here to stay. I like it."

McLeod glanced at him out of the corners of his eyes. "Glad to have you, son. This sure ain't no country for a young feller, though. It's a huntin' an' fishin' country, but no women here, an' no likker. Nothin' much to do, all said an' done."

Casady unsaddled in silence. It was better, though, than a run-in with Vorys, he thought. At least, nobody here knew he was yellow. They liked him and he was one of them, but he was careful.

"Ain't more trouble down below, is there? That Vorys cuttin' up much?" The old man noted the gun Rock was wearing for the trip.

"Some. I hear the boys talkin' about him."

"Never seen him yourself?" Cat asked quizzically. "I been thinkin' ever since you come up here, son. Might be a good thing for this country if you did have trouble with Vorys. You're nigh as big as him, an' you move like a catamount. An' me, I know 'em! Never seen a man lighter on his feet than you."

"Not me," Rock spoke stiffly. "I'm a peace-lovin' man, Cat. I want no trouble with anybody."

McLeod studied the matter as he worked over his hide. For a long time now he had known something was bothering Rock Casady. Perhaps this last remark, that he wanted no trouble with anybody, was the answer?

Cat McLeod was a student of mankind as well as the animals upon whom he practiced his trade. In a lifetime of living along the frontier and in the world's far places, he had learned a lot about men who liked to live alone, and about men who sought the wilderness. If it was true that Rock wanted no trouble, it certainly was not from lack of ability to handle it.

There had been that time when Cat had fallen, stumbling to hands and knees. Right before him, not three feet from his face and much nearer his outstretched hands lay one of the biggest rattlers Cat had ever seen. The snake's head jerked back above its coil, and then, with a gun's roar blasting in his ears, that head was gone and the snake was a writhing mass of coils, showing only a bloody stumb where the head had been!

Cat had gotten to his feet gray faced and turned. Rock Casady was thumbing a shell into his gun. The young man grinned.

"That was a close one!" he had said cheerfully.

McLeod had dusted off his hands, staring at Casady. "I've heard of men drawin' faster'n a snake could strike, but that's the first time I ever seen it!"

Since then he had seen that .44 shoot the heads off quail and he had seen a quick hip shot with the rifle break a deer's neck.

Now his mind reverted to their former topic. "If that Vorys is tied in with some smart hombre, there'll be hell to pay! Pete was never no great shakes for brains, but he's tough, tough as all get out! With somebody to think for him, he'll make this country unfit to live in!"

Later that night, McLeod looked over his shoulder from the fire. "You know," he said, "if I was wantin' a spread of my own, an' didn't care much for folks, like you, I'd go down into the Pleasant Valley Outlet, south of here. Lonely, but she's sure grand country!"

Two days later Rock was mending a bridle when Sue Landon walked over to him. She wore jeans and a boy's shirt, and her eyes were bright and lovely.

"Hi!" she said brightly. "You're the new hand? You certainly keep out of the way. All this time on the ranch and I never met you before!"

He grinned shyly. "Just a quiet hombre, I reckon," he said. "If I had it my way I'd be over there with Cat all the time."

"Then you won't like the job I have for you!" she said. "To ride into Three Lakes with me, riding herd on a couple of pack horses."

"Three Lakes?" He looked up so sharply it startled her. "Into town? I never go into town, ma'am. I don't like the place. Not any town."

"Why, that's silly! Anyway, there's no one else, and Uncle Frank won't let me go alone with Pete Vorys around."

"He wouldn't bother a girl, would he?"

"You sure don't know Pete Vorys!" Sue returned grimly. "He does pretty much what he feels like and everybody's afraid to say anything about it. Although," she added, "with this new partner he's got he's toned down some. But come on—you'll go?"

Reluctantly, he got to his feet. She looked at him curiously, not a little piqued. Any other hand on the ranch would have jumped at the chance, and here she had deliberately made sure there were no others available before going to him. Her few distant glimpses of Rock Casady had excited her interest, and she wanted to know him better.

Yet as the trail fell behind them, she had to admit she was getting no place. For shyness there was some excuse, although usually even the most bashful hand lost it when alone with her. Rock Casady was almost sullen and all she could get out of him were monosyllables.

The truth was that the nearer they drew to Three Lakes the more worried Rock grew. It had been six months since he had been in a town, and while it was improbable he would see anyone he knew, there was always a chance. Cowhands were notoriously footloose and fancy free. Once the story of his backing out of a gunfight got around, he would be through in this country, and he was tired of running.

Yet Three Lakes looked quiet enough as they ambled

placidly down the street and tied up in front of the general store. He glanced at Sue tentatively.

"Ma'am," he said, "I'd sure appreciate it if you didn't stay too long. Towns make me nervous."

She looked at him, more than slightly irritated. Her trip with him, so carefully planned, had thus far come to nothing, although she had to admit he was the finest looking man she had ever seen, and his smile was quick and attractive.

"I won't be long. Why don't you go have a drink? It might do you good!" She said the last sentence a little sharply, and he looked quickly at her, but she was already flouncing into the store, as well as any girl could flounce in jeans.

Slowly he built a cigarette, studying the Hackamore Saloon over the way. He had to admit he was tempted, and probably he was foolish to think that he would get into trouble or that anyone would know him. Nevertheless, he sat down suddenly on the edge of the board walk and lighted his smoke.

He was still sitting there when he heard the sound of booted heels on the boardwalk, and then he heard a raucous voice.

"He! Lookit here! One of them no 'count Three Spokers in town! I didn't think any of them had the sand!"

In spite of himself, he looked up, knowing instantly that this man was Pete Vorys.

He was broad in the shoulder, with narrow hips. He had a swarthy face with dark, brilliant eyes. That he had been drinking was obvious but he was far from drunk. With him were two tough-looking hands, both grinning cynically at him.

Vorys was spoiling for a fight. He had never been

whipped and doubted there lived a man who could whip him in a tooth-and-nail knock-down and drag-out battle. This Three Spoker looked big enough to be fun.

"That's a rawhide outfit, anyway," Vorys sneered. "I've a mind to ride out there sometime, just for laughs. Wonder where they hooked this ranny?"

Despite himself, Rock was growing angry. He was not wearing a gun, and Vorys was. He took the cigarette out of his mouth and looked at it. Expecting trouble, a crowd was gathering. He felt his neck growing red.

"Hey, you!" Vorys booted him solidly in the spine, and the kick hurt. At the same time he slapped Casady with his sombrero. Few things are more calculated to enrage a man.

Rock came to his feet with a lunge. As he turned, with his right palm he grabbed the ankle of Vorys' boot, and with his left fist he smashed him in the stomach, jerking up on the leg. The move was so sudden, so totally unexpected that there was no chance to spring back. Pete Vorys hit the boardwalk flat on his shoulder blades!

A whoop of delight went up from the crowd and for an instant, Pete Vorys lay stunned. Then with an oath he came off the walk, lunging to his feet.

Rock sprang back, his hands wide. "I'm not packin' a gun!" he yelled.

"I don't need a gun!" Vorys yelled. It was the first time he had ever hit the ground in a fight and he was furious.

He stepped in, driving a left to the head. Rock was no boxer. Indeed, he had rarely fought except in fun. He took that blow now, a stunning wallop on the cheekbone. At the same moment, he let go with a wicked right swing. The punch caught Vorys on the chin and rocked him to his heels.

More astonished than hurt, he sprang in and threw two swings for Rock's chin, and Casady took them both coming in. A tremendous light seemed to burst in his brain, but the next instant he had Pete Vorys in his hands. Grabbing him by the collar and the belt, he heaved him to arm's length overhead and hurled him into the street. Still dazed from the punches he had taken, he sprang after the bigger man, and seizing him before he could strike more than an ineffectual punch, swung him to arm's length overhead again, and slammed him into the dust!

Four times he grabbed the hapless bully and hurled him to the ground while the crowd whooped and cheered. The last time, his head clearing, he grabbed Vorys' shirt front with his left hand and swung three times into his face, smashing his nose and lips. Then he lifted the man and heaved him into the water tank with such force that water showered around him.

Beside himself, Rock wheeled on the two startled men who had walked with Vorys. Before either could make a move, he grabbed them by their belts. One swung on Rock's face, but he merely ducked his head and heaved. The man's feet flew up and he hit the ground on his back. Promptly, Rock stacked the other atop him.

The man started to get up, and Rock swung on his face, knocking him into a sitting position. Then grabbing him, he heaved him into the water tank with Vorys who was scrambling to get out. Then he dropped the third man into the pool and putting a hand in Vorys' face, shoved him back.

For an instant then, while the street rocked with cheers and yells of delight, he stood, panting and staring. Suddenly, he was horrified. In his rage he had not thought of what this would mean, but suddenly he knew that they would be hunting him now with guns. He must face a shoot-out, or skip the country!

Wheeling, he shoved through the crowd, aware that someone was clinging to his arm. Looking down, he saw Sue beside him. Her eyes were bright with laughter and pride.

"Oh, Rock! That was wonderful. Just *wonderful!*"

"Let's get out of town!" he said quickly. "Now!"

So pleased was she by the discomfiture of Pete Vorys and his hands by a Three Spoker that she thought nothing of his haste. His eye swelling and his nose still dripping occasional drops of blood, they hit the trail for the home ranch. All the way, Sue babbled happily over his standing up for the Three Spoke, and what it meant, and all the while all he could think of was the fact that on the morrow Vorys would be looking for him with a gun.

He could not face him. It was far better to avoid a fight than to prove himself yellow, and if he fled the country now, they would never forget what he had done, and always make excuses for him. If he stayed behind and showed his yellow streak, he would be ruined.

Frank Stockman was standing on the steps when they rode in, and he took one look at Rock's battered face and torn shirt and come off the steps.

"What happened?" he demanded. "Was it that Pete Vorys again?"

Tom Bell and two other hands were walking up from the bunkhouse, staring at Rock. But already, while he stripped the saddles from the horses, Sue Landon was telling the story, and it lost nothing in the telling. Rock Casady of the Three Spoke had not only whipped Pete Vorys soundly, but he had ducked Pete and two of his tough hands in the Three Lakes' water tank!

The hands crowded around him, crowing and happy, slapping him on the back and grinning. Sandy Kane gripped his hand.

"Thanks, pardner," he said grimly, "I don't feel so bad now!"

Rock smiled weakly, but inside he was sick. It was going to look bad, but he was pulling out. He said nothing, but after supper he got his own horse and threw the saddle aboard, then rustled his gear. When he was all packed, he drew a deep breath and walked toward the ranchhouse.

Stockman was sitting on the wide veranda with Bell and Sue. She got up when he drew near, her eyes bright. He avoided her glance, suddenly aware of how much her praise and happiness meant to him. In his weeks on the Three Spoke, while he had never talked to her before today, his eyes had followed her every move.

"How are you, son?" Stockman asked jovially. "You've made this a red letter day on the Three Spoke! Come up an' sit down! Bell was just talking here, he says he needs a segundo, an' I reckon he's right. How'd you like the job? Eighty a month?"

He swallowed. "Sorry, boss. I got to be movin'. I want my time."

"You *what?*" Bell took the pipe from his mouth and stared.

"I got to roll my hoop," he said stiffly. "I don't want trouble."

Frank Stockman came quickly to his feet. "But listen, man!" he protested. "You've just whipped the best man around this country! You've made a place for yourself here! The boys think you're great! So do I! So does Tom! As for Sue here, all she's done is talk about how wonderful you are! Why, son, you came in here a drifter, an' now you've made a place for yourself! Stick around! We need men like you!"

Despite himself, Casady was wavering. This was what he had always wanted, and wanted now, since the bleak months of his lonely riding, more than ever. A place where he was at home, men who liked him, and a girl. . . .

"Stay on," Stockman said more quietly. "You can handle any trouble that comes, and I promise you, the Three Spoke will back any play you make! Why, with you to head 'em we can run Pete Vorys and that slick partner of his, that Ben Kerr, clean out of the country!"

Casady's face blanched. *"Who? Did you say, Ben Kerr?"*

"Why, sure!" Stockman stared at him curiously, aware of the shocked expression on Rock's face. "Ben Kerr's the hombre who come in here to side Vorys! He's the smart one who's puttin' all those fancy ideas on Pete's head! He's a brother-in-law of Vorys, or something!"

Ben Kerr—here!

That settled it. He could not stay now. There was no time to stay. His mind leaped ahead. Vorys would tell his story, of course. His name would be mentioned, and if not his name, his description. Kerr would know, and he wouldn't waste time. Why, even now. . . !

"Give me my money!" Casady said sharply. "I'm movin' out right now! Thanks for all you've offered, but I'm ridin'! I want no trouble!"

Stockman's face stiffened. "Why, sure," he said, "if you feel that way about it!" He took a roll of bills from his pocket and coolly paid over the money, then abruptly he turned his back and walked inside.

Casady wheeled, his heart sick within him, and started for the corral. He heard running steps behind him, then a light touch on his arm. He looked down, his eyes miserable, into Sue's face.

"Don't go, Rock!" she pleaded gently. "Please don't go! We all want you to stay!"

He shook his head. "I can't Sue! I can't stay here. I want no gun trouble!"

There—it was out.

She stepped back and slowly her face changed. Girl that she was, she still had grown up in the tradition of the West. A man fought his battles with gun or fist, he did not run away.

"Oh?" Her amazed contempt cut him like a whip. "So that's it? You're afraid to face a gun? Afraid of your life?" She stared at him. "Why, Rock Casady," her voice lifted as realization broke over her, "you're *yellow!*"

Hours later, far back in the darkness of night in the mountains, her words rang in his ears. She had called him yellow! She had called him a coward!

Rock Casady, sick at heart, rode slowly into the darkness. At first he rode with no thought but to escape, and then as his awareness began to return, he studied the situation. Lee's Ferry was northeast, and to the south he was bottled by the Colorado Canyon. North it was mostly Vorys' range and west lay Three Lakes and the trails leading to it. East the Canyons fenced him off also, but east lay a lonely, little-known country, ridden only by Cat McLeod in his wanderings after varmints that preyed upon Three Spoke cattle. In that wilderness he might find someplace to hole up. Cat still had plenty of supplies, and he could borrow some from him. . . . Suddenly he remembered the canyon Cat had mentioned, the Pleasant Valley Outlet.

67

He would not go near Cat. There was game enough, and he had packed away a few things in the grub line when he had rolled his soogan. He found an intermittant stream that trailed down a ravine toward Kane Canyon, and followed it. Pleasant Valley Outlet was not far south of Kane. It would be a good hideout. After a few weeks, when the excitement was over, he could slip out of the country.

In a lonely canyon that opened from the south wall into Pleasant Valley Canyon, he found a green and lovely spot. There was plenty of driftwood and a cave hollowed from the Kaibab sandstone by wind and water. There he settled down. Days passed into weeks, and he lived on wild game, berries, and fish. Yet his mind kept turning northwestward toward the Three Spoke, and his thoughts gave him no rest.

On an evening almost three weeks after his escape from the Three Spoke, he was putting his coffee on when he heard a slight sound. Looking up he saw old Cat McLeod grinning at him.

"Howdy, son!" he chuckled. "When you head for the tall timber you sure do a job of it! My land! I thought I'd never find you! No more trail'n trout swimmin' up-stream!"

Rock rose stiffly. "Howdy, Cat. Just put the coffee on." He averted his eyes, and went about the business of preparing a meal.

Cat seated himself, seemingly unhurried and undisturbed by his scant welcome. He got out his pipe and stuffed it full of tobacco. He talked calmly and quietly about game and fish, and the mountain trails.

"Old Mormon crossin' not far from here," he said, "I could show you where it is."

After they had eaten, McLeod leaned back against a

rock. "Lots of trouble back at the Three Spoke. I reckon you was the smart one, pullin' out when you did."

Casady made no response, so McLeod continued. "Pete Vorys was some beat up. Two busted ribs, busted nose, some teeth gone. Feller name of Ben Kerr came out to the Three Spoke huntin' you. Said you was a yella dog an' he knowed you of old. He laughed when he said that, an' said the whole Three Spoke outfit was yella. Stockman, he wouldn't take that, so he went for his gun. Kerr shot him."

Rock's head came up with a jerk. "Shot Stockman? He killed him?" There was horror in his voice. This was his fault—*his!*

"No, he ain't dead. He's sure bad off, though. Kerr added injury to insult by runnin' off a couple of hundred head of Three Spoke stock. Shot one hand doin' it."

A long silence followed in which the two men smoked moodily. Finally, Cat looked across the fire at Rock.

"Son, there's more'n one kind of courage, I say. I seen many a dog stand up to a grizzly that would high-tail it from a skunk. Back yonder they say you're yella. Me, I don't figure it so."

"Thanks, Cat," Rock replied simply, miserably. "Thanks a lot, but you're wrong. I am yellow."

"Reckon it takes pretty much of a man to say that, son. But from what I hear you sure didn't act it against Pete an' his riders. You walloped the tar out of them!"

"With my hands it's different. It's—it's—guns."

McLeod was silent. He poked a twig in the fire and relighted his pipe.

"Ever kill a man, son?" His eyes probed Rock's, and he saw the young rider's head nod slowly. "Who was it? How'd it happen?"

69

"It was—" he looked up, his face drawn and pale. "I killed my brother, Cat."

McLeod was shocked. His old eyes went wide. "You killed your brother? Your *own* brother?"

Rock Casady nodded. "Yeah," he said bitterly, "my own brother. The one person in this world that really mattered to me!"

Cat stared, then slowly his brow puckered. "Son," he said, "why don't you tell me about it? Get it out of your system, like."

For a long while Rock was silent, then he started to speak.

"It was down in Texas. We had a little spread down there, Jack and me. He was a shade older, but alway protectin' me, although I sure didn't need it. The finest man who ever walked, he was.

"Well, we had us a mite of trouble, an' this here Ben Kerr was the ringleader. I had trouble with Ben, and he swore to shoot me on sight. I was a hand with a gun, like you know, an' I was ready enough to fight, them days. One of the hands told me, an' without a word to Jack, I lit into the saddle an' headed for town.

"Kerr was gun-slick, but I wasn't worried. I knew that I didn't have scarcely a friend in town, an' that his whole outfit would be there. It was me against them, an' I went into town with two guns, an' sure enough on the prod.

"It was gettin' late when I hit town. A man I knowed told me Ben was around with his outfit and that nobody was goin' to back me one bit, them all bein' scared of Ben's boys. He told me, too, that Ben Kerr would shoot me in the back as soon as not he bein' that kind.

"I went huntin' him. Kidlike, an' never in no fight before, I was jumpy, mighty jumpy. The light was bad. All of a sudden, I saw one of Ben's boys step out of a door ahead of me. He called out, 'Here he is, Ben! Take him!' Then I heard runnin' feet behind me, heard 'em slide to a halt, an' I wheeled, drawin' as I turned, an' fired." His voice sank to a whisper.

Cat, leaning forward, said, "You shot? An' then? . . ."

"It was Jack. It was my own brother. He'd heard I was in town alone an' he come runnin' to back me up. I drilled him dead center!"

Cat McLeod stared up at the young man, utterly appalled. In his kindly old heart he could only guess at the horror that must have filled Casady, then scarcely more than a boy, when he had looked down into that still, dead face and seen his brother.

"Gosh, son." He shook his head in amazed sympathy. "It ain't no wonder you hate gun fights! It sure ain't! But . . . ?" He scowled. "I still don't see . . . " His voice trailed away.

Rock drew a deep breath. "I sold out then, and left the country. Went to ridin' for an outfit near El Paso. One night I come into town with the other hands, an' who do I run into but Ben Kerr. He thought I ran because I was afraid of him, an' he got tough. He called me—right in front of the outfit. I was goin' to draw, but all I could see there in front of me was Jack, with that blue hole between his eyes! I turned and ran."

Cat McLeod stared at Rock, then into the fire. It was no wonder, he reflected. He probably would have run too. If he had drawn he would have been firing on the image of his brother. It would have been like killing him over again.

"Son," he said slowly, "I know how you feel, but stop a minute an' think about Jack, this brother of yours. He always protected you, you say. He always stood up

71

for you. Now don't you suppose he'd understand? You thought you was all alone in that town. You'd every right to think that was Ben Kerr behind you. I would have thought so, an' I wouldn't have wasted no time shootin', neither.

"You can't run away from yourself. You can't run no further. Someday you got to stand an' face it, an' it might as well be now. Look at it like this: Would your brother want you livin' like this? Hunted and scared? He sure wouldn't! Son, ever' man has to pay his own debt, an' live his own life. Nobody can do it for you, but if I was you, I'd sort of figure my brother was dead because of *Ben Kerr,* and I'd stop runnin'!"

Rock looked up slowly. "Yeah," he agreed, "I see that plain. But what if when I stepped out to meet him, *I look up an' see Jack's face again?*"

His eyes dark with horror, Rock Casady turned and plunged downstream, stumbling, swearing in his fear and loneliness and sorrow.

At daylight, old Cat McLeod opened his eyes. For an instant, he lay still. The he realized where he was, and what he had come for, and he turned his head. Rock Casady, his gear and horse, were gone. Stumbling to his feet, McLeod slipped on his boots and walked out in his red flannels to look at the trail.

It headed south, away from Three Lakes, and away from Ben Kerr. Rock Casady was running again.

The trail south to the canyon was rough and rugged. The palouse was sure-footed and had a liking for the mountains, yet seemed undecided, as though the feeling persisted that he was going the wrong way.

Casady stared bleakly ahead, but he saw little of the orange and red of the sandstone cliffs. He was seeing again Frank Stockman's strong, kindly face, and remembering his welcome at the Three Spoke. He was remembering Sue's hand on his sleeve and her quick smile, and old Tom Bell, gnarled and worn with handling cattle and men. He drew up suddenly and turned the horse on the narrow trail. He was going back.

"Jack," he said suddenly aloud, "stick with me, boy. I'm sure goin' to need you now!"

* * *

Sandy Kane, grim-lipped and white of face, dismounted behind the store. Beside him was Sue Landon.

"Miss Sue," he said, "you get that buyin' done fast. Don't let none of that Vorys crowd see you. They've sure taken this town over since they shot the boss."

"All right, Sandy." She looked at him bravely, then squeezed the older man's hand. "We'll make it all right." Her blue eyes darkened. "I wish I'd been a man, Sandy. Then the boys would come in and clean up this outfit!"

"Miss Sue," he said gently, "don't fret none. Our boys are just honest cowhands. We don't have a gunfighter in the lot, nobody who could stand up to Kerr or Vorys. No man minds a scrap, but it would be plain suicide!"

The girl started to enter the store, then caught the cowboy's hand.

"Sandy," she said faintly, "look!"

A tall man with broad shoulders had swung down before the store. He tied his horse with a slip knot, and hitched his guns into place. Rock Cassady, his hard young face bleak and desperate, stared carefully along the street.

It was only three blocks long, this street. It was dusty

73

and warm with the noon-day sun. The gray-fronted buildings looked upon the dusty canal that separated them, and a few saddled horses stamped lazily, flicking their tails at casual flies. It was like that other street, so long ago.

Casady pulled the flat brim of his black hat a little lower over his eyes. Inside he felt sick and faint. His mouth was dry. His tongue trembled when it touched his lips. Up the street a man saw him and got slowly to his feet, staring as if hypnotized. The man backed away, then dove into the Hackamore Saloon.

Rock Casady took a deep breath, drew his shoulders back, and started slowly down the walk. He seemed in a trance where only the sun was warm and the air was still. Voices murmured. He heard a gasp of astonishment, for these people remembered that he had whipped Pete Vorys, and they knew what he had come for.

He wore two guns now, having dug the other gun and belt from his saddlebags to join the one he had only worn in the mountains. A door slammed somewhere.

Ben Kerr stared at the face of the man in the door of the saloon.

"Ben, here comes that yellow backed Casady! And he's wearin' a gun!"

"He is, is he?" Kerr tossed off his drink. "Fill that up, Jim! I'll be right back. This will only take a minute!"

He stepped out into the street. "Come to get it this time?" he shouted tauntingly. "or are you runnin' again?"

Rock Casady made no reply. His footsteps echoed hollowly on the board walk, and he strode slowly, finishing his walk at the intersecting alley, stepping into the dust, then up on the walk again.

Ben Kerr's eyes narrowed slightly. Some sixth sense warned him that the man who faced him had subtly changed. He lifted his head a little, and stared, then he shrugged off the feeling and stepped out from the building.

"All right, Yella-Belly! If you want it!" His hand swept down in a flashing arc and his gun came up.

Rock Casady stared down the street at the face of Ben Kerr, and it was only the face of Kerr. In his ear was Jack's voice: "Go ahead, kid! Have at it!"

Kerr's gun roared and he felt the hot breath of it bite at his face. And then suddenly, Rock Casady laughed! Within him all was light and easy, and it was almost carelessly that he stepped forward. Suddenly the .44 began to roar and buck in his hand, leaping like a live thing within his grasp. Kerr's gun flew high in the air, his knees buckled, and he fell forward on his face in the dust.

Rock Casady turned quickly toward the Hackamore. Pete Vorys stood in the door, shocked to stillness.

"All right, Pete! Do you want it or are you leavin' town?"

Vorys stared from Kerr's riddled body to the man holding the gun.

"Why, I'm leavin' town!" Vorys said. "That's my roan, right there. I'll just . . ." As though stunned, he started to mount, and Rock's voice arrested him.

"No, Pete. You walk. You hoof it. And start now!"

The bully of Three Lakes wet his lips and stared, then his eyes shifted to the body in the street.

"Sure, Rock," he said, taking a step back. "I'll hoof it." Turning, stumbling a little, he started to walk. As he moved, his walk grew swifter and swifter as though something followed in his tracks.

Rock turned and looked up, and Sue Landon was standing on the boardwalk.

"Oh, Rock! You came back!"

"Don't reckon I ever really left, Sue," he said slowly. "My heart's been right here, all the time!"

She caught his arm, and the smile in her eyes and on her lips was bright. He looked down at her.

Then he said aloud, "Thanks, Jack!"

She looked up quickly. "What did you say?"

He grinned at her. "Sue," he said, "did I ever tell you about my brother? He was one grand hombre! Someday, I'll tell you." They walked back toward the horses, her hand on his arm.

FOUR CARD DRAW

When a man drew four cards he could expect something like this to happen. Ben Taylor had probably been right when he told him his luck had run out. Despite that, he had a place of his own, and come what may, he was going to keep it.

Nor was there any fault to find with the place. From the moment Allen Ring rode his claybank into the valley he knew he was coming home. This was it, this was the place. Here he would stop. He'd been tumbleweeding all over the West now for ten years, and it was time he stopped if he ever did, and this looked like his fence corner.

Even the cabin looked good, although Taylor told him the place had been empty for three years. It looked solid and fit, and while the grass was waist high all over the valley, and up around the house, he could see trails through it, some of them made by unshod ponies, which mean wild horses, and some by deer. Then there were the tracks of a single shod horse, always the same one.

Those tracks always led right up to the door, and they stopped there, yet he could see that somebody with mighty small feet had been walking up to peer into the windows. Why would a person want to look into a window more than once? The window of an empty cabin? He had gone up and looked in himself, and all he saw was a dusty, dark interior with a ray of light from the opposite window, a table, a couple of chairs, and a fine old fireplace that had been built by skilled hands.

"You never built that fireplace, Ben Taylor," Ring had muttered, "you who never could handle anything but a running iron or a deck of cards. You never built anything in your life as fine and useful as that."

The cabin sat on a low ledge of grass backed up against the towering cliff of red rock, and the spring was not more than fifty feet away, a stream that came out of the rock and trickled pleasantly into a small basin before spilling out and winding throughtfully down the valley to join a larger stream, a quarter of a mile away.

There were some tall spruces around the cabin, a couple of sycamores and a cottonwood near the spring. Some gooseberry bushes, too, and a couple of apple trees. The trees had been pruned.

"And you never did that, either, Ben Taylor!" Allen Ring said soberly. "I wish I knew more about this place."

Time had fled like a scared antelope, and with the scythe he found in the pole barn he cut off the tall grass around the house, patched up the holes in the cabin where the pack rats had got in, and even thinned out the bushes—it had been several years since they had been touched—and repaired the pole barn.

The day he picked to clean out the spring was the day Gail Truman rode up to the house. He had been putting the finishing touches on a chair bottom he was making when he heard a horse's hoof strike stone, and he straightened up to see the girl sitting on the red pony. She was staring open mouthed at the stacked hay from the grass he had cut, and the washed windows of the house. He saw her swing down and run up to the window, and dropping his tools he strolled up.

"Huntin' somebody, Ma'am?"

She wheeled and stared at him, her wide blue eyes accusing. "What are you doing here?" she demanded. "What do you mean by moving in like this?"

He smiled, but he was puzzled, too. Ben Taylor had said nothing about a girl, especially a girl like this. "Why, I own the place!" he said. "I'm fixin' it up so's I can live here."

"You own it?" Her voice was incredulous, agonized. "You couldn't own it! You couldn't. The man who owns this place is gone, and he would never sell it! Never!"

"He didn't exactly sell it, Ma'am," Ring said gently, "he lost it to me in a poker game. That was down Texas way."

She was horrified. "In a poker game? Whit Bayly in a poker game? I don't believe it!"

"The man I won it from was called Ben Taylor, Ma'am." Ring took the deed from his pocket and opened it. "Come to think of it, Ben did say that if anybody asked about Whit Bayly to say that he died down in the Guadaloupes—of lead poisoning."

"Whit Bayly is dead?" The girl looked stunned. "You're sure? Oh!"

Her face went white and still and something in it

81

seemed to die. She turned with a little gesture of despair and stared out across the valley, and his eyes followed hers. It was strange, Allen Ring told himself, that it was the first time he had looked just that way, and he stood there, caught up by something nameless, some haunting sense of the familiar.

Before him lay the tall grass of the valley, turning slightly now with the brown of autumn, and to his right a dark stand of spruce, standing stiffly, like soldiers on parade, and beyond them the swell of the hill, and further to the right the hill rolled up and stopped, and beyond lay a wider valley fading away into the vast purple and mauve of distance, and here and there spotted with the golden candles of cottonwoods, their leaves bright yellow with nearing cold.

There was no word for this, it was a picture, yet a picture of which a man could only dream and never reproduce.

"It—it's beautiful, isn't it?" he said.

She turned on him, and for the first time she seemed really to look at him, a tall young man with a shock of rust brown hair and sombre gray eyes, having about him the look of a rider and a look of a lonely man.

"Yes, it is beautiful. Oh, I've come here so many times to see it, the cabin, too. I think this is the most lovely place I have ever seen. I used to dream about—" She stopped, suddenly confused. "Oh, I'm sorry. I shouldn't talk so."

She looked at him soberly "I'd better go. I guess this is yours now."

He hesitated. "Ma'am," he said sincerely, "the place is mine, and sure enough, I love it. I wouldn't swap this place for anything. But that view, that belongs to no man. It belongs to whoever looks at it with eyes to see it, so you come any time you like, and look all you please."

Ring grinned. "Fact is," he said, "I'm aimin' to fix the place up inside, an' I'm sure no hand at such things. Maybe you could sort of help me. I'd like it kind of homey like." He flushed. "You see, I sort of lived in bunkhouses all my life, an' never had no such place."

She smiled with a quick understanding and sympathy. "Of course! I'd love to, only—" her face sobered, "you won't be able to stay here. You haven't seen Ross Bilton yet, have you?"

"Who's he?" Ring asked, curiously. He nodded toward the horsemen he saw approaching. "Is this the one?"

She turned quickly, and nodded. "Be careful! He's the town marshal. The men with him are Ben Hagen and Stan Brule."

Brule he remembered—but would Brule remember him?

"By the way, my name is Allen Ring," he said, low voiced.

"I'm Gail Truman. My father owns the Tall T brand."

Bilton was a big man with a white hat. Ring decided he didn't like him and that the feeling was going to be mutual. Brule he knew, so the stocky man was Ben Hagen. Brule had changed but little, some thinner, maybe, but his hatchet face as lean and poisonous as always.

"How are you, Gail?" Bilton said briefly. "Is this a friend of yours?"

Allen Ring liked to get his cards on the table. "Yes, a friend of hers, but also the owner of the place."

"You own Red Rock?" Bilton was incredulous. "That

will be very hard to prove, my friend. Also, this place is under the custody of the law.''

"Whose law?" Ring wanted to know. He was aware that Brule was watching him, wary but uncertain as yet.

"Mine. I'm the town marshal. There was a murder committed here, and until that murder is solved and the killer brought to justice this place will not be touched. You have already seen fit to make changes, but perhaps the court will be lenient.''

"You're the town marshal?" Allen Ring shoved his hat back on his head and reached for his tobacco. "That's mighty interestin'. Howsoever, let me remind you that you're out of town right now.''

"That makes no difference!" Bilton's voice was sharp. Ring could see that he was not accustomed to being told off. That his orders were usually obeyed. "You will get off this place before nightfall!"

"It makes a sight of difference to me," Allen replied calmly. "I bought this place by stakin' everything I had against it in a poker game. I drew four cards to win, a nine to match one I had, and three aces. It was a fool play that paid off. I registered the deed. She's mine legal. I know of no law that allows a place to be kept idle because there was a murder committed on it. If after three years it hasn't been solved, I suggest the town get a new marshal.''

Ross Bilton was angry, but he kept himself under control. "I've warned you, and you've been told to leave. If you do not leave, I'll use my authority to move you.''

Ring smiled. "Now listen, Bilton! You might pull that stuff on some folks that don't like trouble! You might bluff somebody into believin' you had the authority to do this. You don't bluff me, an' I simply don't scare—do I Brule?"

84

He turned on Brule so sharply that the man stiffened in his saddle, his hand poised as though to grab for a gun. The breed's face stiffened with irritation, and then recognition came to him. "Allen Ring!" he said. "You again!"

"That's right, Brule. Only this time I'm not takin' cattle through the Indian Nation. Not pushin' them by that ratty bunch of rustlers an' highbinders you rode with." Ring turned his eyes toward Bilton. "You're the law? An' you ride with *him?* Why, the man's wanted in ever' county in Texas for everythin' from murder to horse theivin'."

Ross Bilton stared at Ring for a long minute. "You've been warned," he said.

"An' I'm stayin'," Ring replied sharply. "And keep your coyotes away, if you come again. I don't like 'em!"

Brule's fingers spread and his lips stiffened with cold fury. Ring watched him calmly. "You know better than that, Brule. Wait until my back is turned. If you reach for a gun I'll blow you out of your saddle."

Stan Brule slowly relaxed his hand, and then wordless, he turned to follow Bilton and Hagen, who had watched with hard eyes.

Gail Truman was looking at him curiously. "Why, Brule was afraid of you!" she exclaimed. "Who are you, anyway?"

"Nobody, Ma'am," he said simply. "I'm no gunfighter, just an hombre who ain't got brains enough to scare proper. Brule knows it. He knows he might beat me, but he knows I'd kill him. He was there when I killed a friend of his, Blaze Garden."

"But—but then you must be a gunman. Blaze Garden

85

was a killer! I've heard Dad and the boys talk about him!"

"No, I'm no gunman. Blaze beat me to the draw. In fact, he got off his first shot before my gun cleared the holster, only he shot too quick and missed. His second and third shots hit me while I was walkin' to him. The third shot wasn't so bad because I was holdin' my fire and gettin' close. He got scared an' stepped back and the third shot was too high. Then I shot and I was close up to him then. One was enough. One is always enough if you place it right."

He gestured at the place. "What's this all about? Mind tellin' me?"

"It's very simple, really. Nothing out here is very involved when you come to that. It seems that there's something out here that brings men to using guns much faster than in other places, and one thing stems from another.

"Whit Bayly owned this place. He was a fixing man, always tinkering and fixing things up. He was a tall, handsome man whom all the girls loved—"

"You, too?" he asked quizzically.

She flushed. "Yes, I guess so, only I'm only eighteen now, and that was three, almost four years ago. I wasn't very pretty, or very noticeable and much too young.

"Sam Hazlitt was one of the richest men in the country around here, and Whit had a run-in with him over a horse. There had been a lot of stealing going on around, and Hazlitt traced some stock of his to this ranch, or so he claimed. Anyway, he accused Bayly of it, and Whit told him not to talk foolish. Furthermore, he told Hazlitt to stay off of his ranch. Well, folks were divided over who was in the right, but Whit had a lot of friends and Hazlitt had four brothers and clannish as all get out.

"Not long after some riders from Buck Hazlitt's ranch came by that way and saw a body lying in the yard, right over near the spring. When they came down to have a look, thinking Whit was hurt, they found Sam Hazlitt, and he'd been shot dead—in the back.

"They headed right for town, hunting Whit, and they found him. He denied it, and they were goin' to hang him, had a rope around his neck, and then I—I—well, I swore he wasn't anywhere near his ranch all day."

"It wasn't true?" Ring asked keenly, his eyes searching the girl's face. She avoided his eyes, flushing even more.

"Not—not exactly. But I knew he wasn't guilty! I just knew he wouldn't shoot a man in the back! I told them he was over to our place, talking with me, and he hadn't time to get back there and kill Sam.

"Folks didn't like it much. Some of them still believed he killed Sam, and some didn't like it because despite the way I said it, they figured he was sparking a girl too young for him. I always said it wasn't that. As a matter of fact, I did see Whit over our way, but the rest of it was lies. Anyway, after a few weeks Whit up and left the country."

"I see—and nobody knows yet who killed Sam Hazlitt?"

"Nobody. One thing that was never understood was what became of Sam's account book—sort of a tally book, but more than that. It was a sort of record he kept of a lot of things, and it was gone out of his pocket. Nobody ever found it, but they did find the pencil Sam used on the sand nearby. Dad always figured Sam lived long enough to write something, but that the killer stole the book and destroyed it."

"How about the hands? Could they have picked it up? Did Bilton question them about that?"

"Oh, Bilton wasn't marshal then! In fact, he was riding for Buck Hazlitt then! He was one of the hands who found Sam's body!"

After the girl had gone Allen Ring walked back to the house and thought the matter over. He had no intention of leaving. This was just the ranch he wanted, and he intended to live right here, yet the problem fascinated him.

Living in the house and looking around the place had taught him a good deal about Whit Bayly. He was, as Gail had said, "a fixin' man," for there were many marks of his handiwork aside from the beautifully made fireplace and the pruned apple trees. He was, Ring was willing to gamble, no murderer.

Taylor had said he died of lead poisoning. Who had killed Bayly? Why? Was it a casual shooting over some rangeland argument, or had he been followed from here by someone on vengeance bent? Or someone who thought he might know too much?

"You'll like the place." Taylor had said—that was an angle he hadn't considered before. Ben Taylor had actually seen this place himself! The more sign he read, the more tricky the trail became, and Allen walked outside and sat down against the cabin wall when his supper was finished, and lighted a smoke.

Stock had been followed to the ranch by Sam Hazlitt. If Whit was not the thief, then who was? Where had the stock been driven? He turned his eyes almost automatically toward the Mogollons, the logical place. His eyes narrowed, and he recalled that one night while playing cards they had been talking of springs and waterholes, and Ben Taylor had talked about Fossil Springs, a huge spring that roared thousands of gallons of water out of the earth.

"Place a man could run plenty of stock," he had said and winked, "and nobody the wiser!"

Those words had been spoken far away and long ago, and the Red Rock ranch had not yet been put on the table; that was months later. There was, he recalled, a Fossil Creek somewhere north of here. And Fossil Creek might flow from Fossil Spring—perhaps Ben Taylor had talked more to effect than he knew. That had been Texas, and this was Arizona, and a casual bunkhouse conversation probably seemed harmless enough.

"We'll see, Ben!" Ring muttered grimly. "We'll see!"

Ross Bilton had been one of the Hazlitt hands at the time of the killing, one of the first on the scene. Now he was town marshal but interested in keeping the ranch unoccupied—why?

None of it made sense, yet actually it was no business of his. Allen Ring thought that over, and decided it was his business in a sense. He now owned the place, and lived on it. If an old murder was to interfere with his living there, it behooved him to know the facts. It was a slight excuse for his curiosity.

Morning came and the day drew on toward noon, and there was no sign of Bilton or Brule. Ring had loaded his rifle and kept it close to hand, and he was wearing two guns, thinking he might need a loaded spare, although he rarely wore more than one. Also, inside the cabin door he had his double barreled shotgun.

The spring drew his attention. At the moment he did not wish to leave the vicinity of the cabin, and that meant a good time to clean out the spring. Not that it needed it, but there loose stones in the bottom of the basin, and some moss. With this removed he would have more water and clearer water. With a wary eye toward the canyon mouth, he began his work.

The sound of an approaching horse drew him erect. His rifle stood against the rocks at hand, and his guns were ready, yet as the rider came into sight, he saw there was only one man, and a stranger.

He rode a fine bay gelding and he was not a young man, but thick and heavy with drooping mustache and kind blue eyes. He drew up.

"Howdy!" he asid affably, yet taking a quick glance around before looking again at Ring. "I'm Rolly Truman, Gail's father."

"It's a pleasure," Ring said, wiping his wet hands on a red bandana. "Nice to know the neighbors." He nodded at the spring. "I picked me a job. That hole's deeper than it looks!"

"Good flow of water," Truman agreed. He chewed his mustache thoughtfully. "I like to see a young man with get up about him, startin' his own spread, willin' to work."

Allen Ring waited. The man was building up to something; what, he knew not. It came then, carefully at first, yet shaping a loop as it drew near.

"Not much range here, of course," Truman added, "you should have more graze. Ever been over in Cedar Basin? Or up along the East Verde bottom? Wonderful land up there, still come wild, but a country where a man could do something with a few white-face cattle."

"No, I haven't seen it," Ring replied. "but I'm satisfied. I'm not land hungry. All I want is a small place, an' this suits me fine."

Truman shifted in his saddle and looked uncomfortable. "Fact is, Son, you're upsettin' a lot of folks by bein' here. What you should do is to move."

"I'm sorry," Ring said flatly, "I don't want to make enemies, but I won this place on a four card draw. Maybe I'm a fatalist, but somehow or other, I think I should stick here. No man's got a right to think he can draw four cards and win anythin', but I did, an' in a plenty rough game. I had everythin' I owned in that pot. Now I got the place."

The rancher sat his horse uneasily, then he shook his head. "Son, you've sure got to move! There's no trouble here now, and if you stay she's liable to open old sores, start more trouble than any of us can stop. Besides, how did Ben Taylor get title to this place? Bayly had no love for him. I doubt if your title will stand up in court."

"As to that I don't know." Ring persisted stubbornly, "I have a deed that's legal enough, and I've registered that deed, an' my brand along with it. I did find out that Bayly had no heirs. So I reckon I'll sit tight until somebody comes along with a better legal claim than mine."

Truman ran his hand over his brow. "Well, I guess I don't blame you much, Son. Maybe I shouldn't have come over, but I know Ross Bilton and his crowd, and I reckon I wanted to save myself some trouble as well as you. Gail, she thinks you're a fine young man. In fact, you're the first man she's ever showed interest in since Whit left, and she was a youngster then. It was a sort of hero worship she had for him. I don't want trouble."

Allen Ring leaned on the shovel and looked up at the older man. "Truman," he said, "are you sure you aren't buyin' trouble by tryin' to avoid it? Just what's your stake in this?"

The rancher sat very still, his face drawn and pale. Then he got down from his horse and sat on a rock. Removing his hat, he mopped his brow.

"Son," he said slowly, "I reckon I got to trust you. You've heard of the Hazlitts. They are a hard, clannish bunch, men who lived by the gun most of their lives. Sam was murdered. Folks all know that when they find out who murdered him and why, there's goin' to be plenty of trouble around here. Plenty."

"Did you kill him?"

Truman jerked his head up. "No! No, you mustn't get that idea, but—well, you know how small ranchers are. There was a sight of rustlin' them days, and the Hazlitts were the big outfit. They lost cows."

"And some of them got your brand?" Ring asked shrewdly.

Truman nodded. "I reckon. Not so many, though. And not only me. Don't get me wrong, I'm not beggin' off the blame. Part of it is mine, all right, but I didn't get many. Eight or ten of us hereabouts slapped brands on Hazlitt stock—and at least five of us have the biggest brands around here now, some as big almost as the Hazlitts."

Allen Ring studied the skyline thoughtfully. It was an old story and one often repeated in the west. When the War Between the States ended, men came home to Texas, and the southwest to find cattle running in thousands, unbranded, and unowned. The first man to slap on a brand was the owner, and no way he could be contested.

Many men grew rich with nothing more than a wide loop and a running iron. Then the unbranded cattle were gone, the ranches had settled into going concerns, and the great days of casual branding had ended, yet there was still free range, and a man with that same loop and a running iron could still build a herd fast.

More than one of the biggest ranchers had begun that way, and many of them continued to brand loose stock wherever found. No doubt that had been true here, and these men like Rolly Truman, good, able men who had fought Indians and built their homes to last, had begun just that way. Now the range was mostly fenced, ranches had narrowed somewhat, but Ring could see what it might mean to open an old sore now.

Sam Hazlitt had been trailing rustlers—he had found out who they were, and where the herds were taken, and he had been shot down from behind. The catch was that the tally book, with his records, was still missing. That tally book might contain evidence as to the rustling done by men who were now pillars of the community, and open them to the vengeance of the Hazlitt outfit.

Often western men threw a blanket over a situation. If a rustler had killed Sam, then all the rustlers involved would be equally guilty. Anyone who lived on this ranch might stumble on that tally book and throw the range into a bloody gun war in which many men now beyond the errors of their youth, with homes, families, and different customs, would die.

It could serve no purpose to blow the lid off the trouble now, yet Allen Ring had a hunch. In their fear of trouble for themselves they might be concealing an even greater crime, aiding a murderer in his escape. There were lines in the face of Rolly Truman that a settled, established rancher should not have.

"Sorry," Ring said, "I'm stayin'. I like this place."

All through the noon hour the tension was building. The air was warm and sultry, and there was a thickening haze over the mountains. There was that hot, thickness in the air that presaged a storm. Yet when he left his coffee to return to work, Ring saw three horsemen coming into the canyon mouth at a running walk. He stopped in the door and touched his lips with his tongue.

They reined up at the door, three hard-bitten, hard-eyed men with rifles across their saddle bows. Men with guns in their holsters and men of a kind that would never turn from trouble. These were men with the bark on, lean fanatics with lips thinned with old bitterness.

The older man spoke first. "Ring, I've heard about you. I'm Buck Hazlitt. These are my brothers, Joe and Dolph. There's talk around that you aim to stay on this place. There's been talk for years that Sam hid his tally book here. We figure the killer got that book and burned it. Maybe he did, and again, maybe not. We want that book. If you want to stay on this place, you stay. But if you find that book, you bring it to us."

Ring looked from one to the other, and he could see the picture clearly. With men like these, hard and unforgiving, it was no wonder Rolly Truman and the other ranchers were worried. The years and prosperity had eased Rolly and his like into comfort and softness, but not there. The Hazlitts were of feudal blood and background.

"Hazlitt," Ring said, "I know how you feel. You lost a brother, and that means somethin', but if that book is still around, which I doubt, and I find it, I'll decide what to do with it all by myself. I don't aim to start a range war. Maybe there's some things best forgotten. The man who murdered Sam Hazlitt ought to pay."

"We'll handle that," Dolph put in grimly. "You find that book, you bring it to us. If you don't—" His eyes hardened. "Well, we'd have to class you with the crooks."

Ring's eyes shifted to Dolph. "Class, if you want," he flared. "I'll do what seems best to me with that book. But all of you folks are plumb proddy over that tally book. Chances are nine out of ten the killer found it and destroyed it."

"I don't reckon he did," Buck said coldly, "because we know he's been back here, a-huntin' it. Him an' his girl."

Ring stiffened. "You mean—?"

"What we mean is our figger, not yours." Buck Hazlitt reined his horse around. "You been told. You bring that book to us. You try to buck the Hazlitts and you won't stay in this country."

Ring had his back up. Despite himself he felt cold anger mounting within him. "Put this in your pipe, friend." he said harshly, "I came here to stay. No Hazlitt will change that. I ain't huntin' trouble but if you bring trouble to me, I'll handle it. I can bury a Hazlitt as easy as any other man!"

Not one of them condescended to notice the remark. Turning their horses they walked them down the canyon and out of it into the sultry afternoon. Allen Ring mopped the sweat from his face, and listened to the deep rumbling of far off thunder, growling among the canyons like a grizzly with a toothache. It was going to rain. Sure as shootin', it was going to rain—a regular gully washer.

There was yet time to finish the job on the spring, so he picked up his shovel and started back for the job. The rock basin was nearly cleaned and he finished removing the few rocks and the moss that had gathered. Then he opened the escape channel a little more to insure a more rapid emptying and filling process in the basin into which the trickle of water fell.

The water emerged from a crack in the rocks and

trickled into the basin and finishing his job, Ring glanced thoughtfully to see if anything remained undone. There was still some moss on the rocks from which the water flowed, and kneeling down, he leaned over to scrape it away and pulling away the last shreds, he noticed a space from which a rock had recently fallen. Pulling more moss away, he dislodged another rock, and there, pushed into a niche, was a small black book!

Sam Hazlit, dying, had evidently managed to shove it back in this crack in the rocks, hoping it would be found by someone not the killer.

Sitting back on his haunches, Ring opened the faded, canvas bound book. A flap crossed over the page ends and the book had been closed by a small tongue that slid into a loop of the canvas cover. Opening the book, he saw the pages were stained, but still legible.

The next instant he was struck by lightning. At least, that was what seemed to happen. Thunder crashed, and something struck him on the skull and he tried to rise and something struck again. He felt a drop of rain on his face and his eyes opened wide and then another blow caught him and he faded out into darkness, his fingers clawing at the grass to keep from slipping down into that velvety, smothering blackness.

He was wet. He turned a little, lying there, thinking he must have left a window open and the rain was—his eyes opened and he felt rain pounding on his face and he stared, not at a boot with a California spur, but at dead brown grass, soaked with rain now, and the glistening smoothness of water-worn stones. He was soaked to the hide.

Struggling to his knees, he looked around, his head heavy, his lips and tongue thick. He blinked at a gray, rain slanted world and at low gray clouds and a distant rumble of thunder following a streak of lightning along the mountain tops.

Lurching to his feet, he stumbled toward the cabin and pitched over the door sill to the floor. Struggling again to his feet he got the door closed and in a vague, misty half world of consciousness he struggled out of his clothes and got his hands on a rough towel and fumblingly dried himself.

He did not think. He was acting purely from vague instinctive realization of what he must do. He dressed again, in dry clothes and dropped at the table. After awhile he sat up and it was dark and he knew he had blacked out again. He lighted a light and nearly dropped it to the floor, then stumbled to the wash basin and splashed his face with cold water. Then he bathed his scalp, feeling tenderly of the lacerations there.

A boot with a California spur.

That was all he had seen. The tally book was gone, and a man wearing a new boot with a California type spur, a large rowel, had taken it. He got coffee on, and while he waited for it he took his guns out and dried them painstakingly, wiping off each shell, then replacing them in his belt with other shells from a box on a shelf.

He reloaded the guns, then slipping into his slicker he went outside for his rifle. Between sips of coffee, he worked over his rifle until he was satisfied, then threw a small pack together, and stuffed his slicker pockets with shotgun shells.

The shotgun was an express gun and short barreled. He slung it from a loop under the slicker. Then he took a lantern and went to the stable and saddled the claybank. Leading the horse outside into the driving rain, he swung into the saddle and turned along the road toward Basin.

There was no letup in the rain. It fell steadily and heavily, yet the claybank slogged along, alternating between a shambling trot and a fast walk. Allen Ring, his chin sunk in the upturned collar of his slicker watched the drops fall from the brim of his Stetson and felt the bump of the shotgun under his coat.

He had seen little of the tally book, but sufficient to know that it would blow the lid off the very range war they were fearing. Knowing the Hazlitts, he knew they would bring fire and gunplay to every home even remotely connected with the death of their brother.

The horse slid down a steep bank and shambled across the wide wash. Suddenly, the distant roar that had been in his ears for some time sprang into consciousness and he jerked his head up. His horse snorted in alarm, and Ring stared, open mouthed at the wall of water towering all of ten feet high, that was rolling down the wash toward him.

With a shrill rebel yell he slapped the spurs to the claybank and the startled horse turned loose with an astounded leap and hit the ground in a dead run. There was no time to slow for the bank of the wash and the horse went up, slipped at the very brink and started to fall back.

Ring hit the ground with both boots, scrambled over the brink, and even as the flood roared down upon them, he heaved on the bridle and the horse cleared the edge and stood trembling. Swearing softly, Ring kicked the mud from his boots and mounted again. Leaving the raging torrent behind him he rode on.

Thick blackness of night and heavy clouds lay upon the town when he sloped down the main street and headed the horse toward the barn. He swung down, handed the bridle to the handy man.

"Rub him down," he said. "I'll be back."

He started for the doors, then stopped, staring at the three horses in neighboring stalls. The liveryman noticed his glance, and looked at him.

"The Hazlitts. They come in about an hour ago, ugly as sin."

Allen Ring stood wide legged, staring grimly out the door. There was a coolness inside him now that he recognized. He dried his hands carefully.

"Bilton in town?" he asked.

"Sure is. Playin' cards over to the Mazatzal Salloon."

"He wear Mex spurs? Big rowels?"

The man rubbed his jaw. "I don't remember. I don't know at all. You watch out," he warned, "folks are on the prod."

Ring stepped out into the street and slogged through the mud to the edge of the boardwalk before the darkened general store. He kicked the mud from his boots and dried his hands again, after carefully unbuttoning his slicker.

Nobody would have a second chance after this. He knew well enough that his walking into the Mazatzal would precipitate an explosion. Only, he wanted to light the fuse himself, in his own way.

He stood there in the darkness alone, thinking it over. They would all be there. It would be like tossing a match into a lot of fused dynamite. He wished then that he was a better man with a gun than he was, or that he had someone to side him in this, but he had always acted alone and would scarcely know how to act with anyone else.

He walked along the boardwalk with long strides, his boots making hard sounds under the steady roar of the rain. He couldn't lace that spur, that boot. Yet he had to. He had to get his hands on that boot.

Four horses stood, heads down in the rain, saddles covered with slickers. He looked at them, and saw they were of three different brands. The window of the Mazatzal was rain wet, yet standing at one side he glanced within.

The long room was crowded and smoky. Men lined the bar, feet on the brass rail. A dozen tables were crowded with card players. Everyone seemed to have taken refuge here from the rain. Picking out the Hazlitt boys, Allen saw them gathered together at the back end of the room. Then he got Ross Bilton pegged. He was at a table playing cards, facing the door. Stan Brule was at this end of the bar, and Hagen was at a table against the wall, the three of them making three points of a flat triangle whose base was the door.

It was no accident. Bilton then, expected trouble, and he was not looking toward the Hazlitts. Yet, on reflection, Ring could see the triangle could center fire from three directions on the Hazlitts as well. There was a man with his back to the door who sat in the game with Bilton. And not far from Hagen, Rolly Truman was at the bar.

Truman was toying with his drink, just killing time. Everybody seemed to be waiting for something.

Could it be he they waited upon? No, that was scarcely to be considered. They could not know he had found the book, although it was certain at least one man in the room knew, and possibly others. Maybe it was just the tension, the building up of feeling over his taking over of the place at Red Rock. Allen Ring carefully turned down the collar of his slicker and wiped his hands dry again.

He felt jumpy, and could feel that dryness in his mouth that always came on him at times like this. He touched his gun butts, then stepped over and opened the door.

Every one looked up or around at once. Ross Bilton held a card aloft and his hand froze in the act of dealing, holding still for a full ten seconds while Ring closed the door. He surveyed the room again, saw Ross play the card and say something in an undertone to the man opposite him. The man turned his head slightly and it was Ben Taylor!

The gambler looked around, his face coldly curious, and for an instant their eyes met across the room, and then Allen Ring started toward him.

There was no other sound in the room, although they could all hear the unceasing roar of the rain of the roof. Ring saw something leap up in Taylor's eyes and his own took on a sardonic glint.

"That was a good hand you dealt me down Texas way," Ring said. "A good hand!"

"You'd better draw more cards," Taylor said, "you're holdin' a small pair!"

Ring's eyes shifted as the man turned slightly. It was the jingle of his spurs that drew his eyes, and there they were, the large rowelled California style spurs, not common here. He stopped beside Taylor so the man had to tilt his head back to look up. Ring was acutely conscious that he was not centered between the fire and Brule and Hagen. The Hazlitts looked on curiously, uncertain as to what was happening.

"Give it to me, Taylor," Ring said quietly, "give it to me now."

There was ice in his voice, and Taylor, aware of the awkwardness of his position, got to his feet, inches away from Ring.

101

"I don't know what you're talking about," he flared.
"No?"

Ring was standing with his feet apart a little, and his hands were breast high, one of them clutching the edge of his raincoat. He hooked with his left from that position, and the blow was too short, too sudden, and too fast for Ben Taylor.

The crack of it on the angle of his jaw was audible, and then Ring's right came up in the gambler's solar plexus and the man's knees sagged. Spinning him around, Ring ripped open his coat with a jerk that scattered buttons across the room, then from an inside pocket he jerked the tally book.

He saw the Hazlitts start at the same instant that Bilton sprang back from the chair, upsetting it.

"Get him!" Bilton roared. "Get him!"

Ring shoved Taylor hard into the table, upsetting it and causing Bilton to spring back to keep his balance, and at the same instant, Ring dropped to a half crouch and turning left he drew with a flash of speed, saw Brule's gun come up at almost the same instant, and then he fired!

Stan Brule was caught with his gun just level and the bullet smashed him on the jaw. The tall man staggered, his face a mask of hatred and astonishment mingled, and then Ring fired again, did a quick spring around with his knees bent, turning completely around in one leap, and firing as his feet hit the floor. He felt Hagen's bullet smash into him, and he tottered, then fired coolly, and swinging as he fired, he caught Bilton right over the belt buckle.

It was fast action, snapping, quick, yet deliberate. The four fired shots had taken less than three seconds.

Stepping back, he scooped the tally book from the floor where it had dropped, then pocketed it. Bilton was on the floor, coughing blood. Hagen had a broken right arm and was swearing in a thick, stunned voice.

Stan Brule had drawn his last gun. He had been dead before he hit the floor. The Hazlitts started forward with a lunge, and Allen Ring took another step backward, dropping his pistol and swinging the shotgun, still hanging from his shoulder, into firing position.

"Get back!" he said thickly. "Get back or I'll kill the three of you! Back—back to where you stood!"

Their faces wolfish, the three stood lean and dangerous, yet the shotgun brooked no refusal and slowly, bitterly and reluctantly, the three moved back, step by step.

Ring motioned with the shotgun. "All of you—along the wall!"

The men rose and moved back, their eyes on him, uncertain, wary, some of them frightened.

Allen Ring watched them go, feeling curiously light-headed and uncertain. He tried to frown away the pain from his throbbing skull, yet there was a pervading weakness from somewhere else.

"My gosh!" Rolly Truman said. "The man's been shot! He's bleeding!"

"Get back!" Ring said thickly.

His eyes shifted to the glowing pot bellied stove, and he moved forward, the shotgun waist high, his eyes on the men who stared at him, awed.

The sling held the gun level, his hand partly supporting it, a finger in the trigger. With his left hand he opened the stove, then fumbled in his pocket.

Buck Hazlitt's eyes bulged. "No!" he roared "No, you don't!"

103

He lunged forward, and Ring tipped the shotgun and fired a blast into the floor, inches ahead of Hazlitt's feet. The rancher stopped so suddenly he almost fell, the shotgun tipped to cover him.

"Back!" Ring said. He swayed on his feet. "Back!" He fished out the tally book and threw it into the flames.

Something like a sigh went through the crowd. They stared, awed as the flames seized hungrily at the opened book, curling around the leaves with hot fingers, turning them brown, then black and to ashes.

Half hypnotized the crowd watched, then Ring's eyes swung to Hazlitt. "It was Ben Taylor killed him," he muttered. "Taylor, an' Bilton was with him. He—he seen it."

"We take your word for it?" Buck Hazlitt demanded furiously.

Allen Ring's eyes widened and he seemed to gather himself. "You want to question it? You want to call me a liar?"

Hazlitt looked at him, touching his tongue to his lips. "No," he said, "I figured it was them."

"I told you true," Ring said, and then his legs seemed to fold up under him and he went to the floor.

The crowd surged forward and Rolly Truman stared at Buck as Hazlitt neared the stove. The big man stared into the flames for a minute, then he closed the door.

"Good!" he said. "Good thing! It's been a torment, that book, like a cloud hangin' over us all!"

The sun was shining through the window when Gail Truman came to see him. He was sitting up in bed, and feeling better. It would be good to be back on the place again, for there was much to do. She came in, slapping her boots with her quirt and smiling.

"Feel better?" she asked brightly. "You certainly look better. You've shaved."

He grinned and rubbed his jaw. "I needed it. Almost two weeks in this bed. I must have been hit bad."

"You lost a lot of blood. It's lucky you've a strong heart."

"It ain't—isn't so strong any more," he said, "I think it's grown mighty shaky here lately."

Gail blushed. "Oh? It has? Your nurse, I suppose?"

"She is pretty, isn't she?"

Gail looked up, alarmed. "You mean, you—"

"No, honey," he said, "you!"

"Oh." She looked at him, then looked down. "Well, I guess—"

"All right?"

She smiled then, suddenly and warmly. "All right."

"I had to ask you," he said. "We had to marry."

"Had to? Why?"

"People would talk, a young, lovely girl like you over at my place all the time—would they think you were looking at the view?

"If they did," she replied quickly, "they'd be wrong!"

"You're telling me?" he asked.

KEEP TRAVELIN',
RIDER

CHAPTER ONE

Guns of Change

When Tack Gentry sighted the weather beaten buildings of the G Bar, he touched spurs to the buckskin and the horse broke into a fast canter that carried the cowhand down the trail and around into the ranch yard. He swung down.

"Hey!" he yelled happily, grinning. "Is that all the welcome I get?"

The door pushed open and a man stepped out on the worn porch. The man had a stubble of a beard and a drooping mustache. His blue eyes were small and narrow.

"Who are yuh?" he demanded. "And what do yuh want?"

"I'm Tack Gentry!" Tack said. "Where's Uncle John?"

"I don't know yuh," the man said, "and I never heard

of no Uncle John. I reckon yuh got onto the wrong spread, youngster."

"Wrong spread?" Tack laughed. "Quit your funnin'! I helped build that house there, and built the corrals by my lonesome, while Uncle John was sick. Where is everybody?"

The man looked at him carefully, then lifted his eyes to a point beyond Tack. A voice spoke from behind the cowhand. "Reckon yuh been gone awhile, ain't yuh?"

Gentry turned. The man behind him was short, stocky and blond. He had a wide, flat face, a small broken nose and cruel eyes.

"Gone? I reckon yes! I've been gone most of a year! Went north with a trail herd to Ellsworth, then took me a job as a segundo on a herd movin' to Wyoming."

Tack stared around, his eyes alert and curious. There was something wrong here, something very wrong. The neatness that had been typical of Uncle John Gentry was gone. The place looked run down, the porch was untidy, the door hung loose on its hinges, even the horses in the corral were different.

"Where's Uncle John?" Tack demanded again. "Quit stallin'!"

The blond man smiled, his lips parting over broken teeth and a hard, cynical light coming into his eyes. "If yuh mean John Gentry, who used to live on this place, he's gone. He drawed on the wrong man and got himself killed."

"What?" Tack's stomach felt like he had been kicked. He stood there, staring. "He *drew* on somebody? *Uncle John?*"

Tack shook his head. "That's impossible! John Gentry was a Quaker. He never lifted a hand in violence against

110

anybody or anything in his life! He never even wore a gun, never owned one!"

"I only know what they tell me," the blond man said, "but we got work to do, and I reckon yuh better slope out of here. And," he added grimly, "if yuh're smart yuh'll keep right on goin', clean out of this country!"

"What do yuh mean?" Tack's thoughts were in a turmoil trying to accustom himself to this change, wondering what could have happened, what was behind it.

"I mean yuh'll find things considerably changed around here. If yuh decide not to leave," he added, "yuh might ride into Sunbonnet and look up Van Hardin or Dick Olney and tell him I said to give yuh all yuh had comin', tell 'em Soderman sent yuh."

"Who's Van Hardin?" Tack asked. The name was unfamiliar.

"Yuh been away all right!" Soderman acknowledged. "Or yuh'd know who Van Hardin is. He runs this country. He's the ramrod, Hardin is. Olney's sheriff."

Tack Gentry rode away from his home ranch with his thoughts in confusion. Uncle John! Killed in a gunfight! Why, that was out of reason! The old man wouldn't fight. He never had, and never would. And this Dick Olney was sheriff! What had beome of Pete Liscomb? No election was due for another year, and Pete had been a good sheriff.

There was only one way to solve the problem and get the whole story, and that was to circle around and ride by the London ranch. Bill could give him the whole story, and besides, he wanted to see Betty. It had been a long time.

The six miles to the headquarters of the London ranch went by swiftly, yet as Tack rode, he scanned the grassy levels along the Maravillas. There were cattle enough, more than he had ever seen on the old G Bar, and all of them wearing the G Bar brand.

He reined in sharply. What the? . . . Why, if Uncle John was dead, the ranch belonged to him! But if that was so, who was Soderman? And what were they doing on his ranch?

Three men were loafing on the wide veranda of the London ranch house when Tack rode up. All their faces were unfamiliar. He glanced warily from one to the other.

"Where's Bill London?" he asked.

"London?" The man in the wide brown hat shrugged. "Reckon he's to home, over in Sunbonnet Pass. He ain't never over here."

"This is his ranch, isn't it?" Tack demanded.

All three men seemed to tense. "His ranch?" The man in the brown hat shook his head. "Reckon yuh're a stranger around here. This ranch belongs to Van Hardin. London ain't got a ranch. Nothin' but a few acres back against the creek over to Sunbonnet Pass. He and that girl of his live there. I reckon though," he grinned suddenly, "she won't be there much longer. Hear tell she's goin' to work in the Longhorn Dance Hall."

"Betty London? In the Longhorn?" Tack exclaimed. "Don't make me laugh, partner! Betty's too nice a girl for that! She wouldn't . . ."

"They got it advertised," the brown hatted man said calmly.

An hour later a very thoughtful Tack Gentry rode up the dusty street of Sunbonnet. In that hour of riding he had been doing a lot of thinking, and he was remembering what Soderman had said. He was to tell Hardin or Olney that Soderman had sent him to get all that was

112

coming to him. Suddenly, that remark took on a new significance.

Tack swung down in front of the Longhorn. Emblazoned on the front of the saloon was a hugh poster announcing that Betty London was the coming attraction, that she would sing and entertain at the Longhorn. Compressing his lips, Tack walked into the saloon.

Nothing was familiar except the bar and the tables. The man behind the bar was squat and fat, his eyes peered at Tack from folds of flesh. "What's it for yuh?" he demanded.

"Rye," Tack said. He let his eyes swing slowly around the room. Not a familiar face greeted him. Shorty Davis was gone. Nick Farmer was not around. These men were strangers, a tight mouthed, hard eyed crew.

Gentry glanced at the bartender. "Any ridin' jobs around here? Driftin' through, and thought I might like to tie in with one of the outfits around here."

"Keep driftin'," the bartender said, not glancing at him. "Everybody's got a full crew."

One door swung open and a tall, clean cut man walked into the room, glancing around. He wore a neat gray suit and a dark hat. Tack saw the bartender's eyes harden, and glanced thoughtfully at the newcomer. The man's face was very thin, and when he removed his hat his ash blond hair was neatly combed.

He glanced around, and his eyes lighted on Tack. "Stranger?" he asked pleasantly. "Then may I buy you a drink? I don't like to drink alone, but haven't sunk so low as to drink with these coyotes."

Tack stiffened, expecting a reaction from some of the seated men, but there was none. Puzzled, he glanced at the blond man, and seeing the cynical good humor in the man's eyes, nodded.

113

"Sure, I'll drink with you."

"My name," the tall man added, "is Anson Childe, by profession, a lawyer, by dint of circumstances, a gambler, and by choice, a student.

"You perhaps wonder," he added, "why these men do not resent my reference to them as coyotes. There are three reasons, I expect. The first is that some subconscious sense of truth makes them appreciate the justice of the term, second, they know I am gifted with considerable dexterity in expounding the gospel of Judge Colt. Third, they know that I am dying of tuberculosis and as a result have no fear of bullets.

"It is not exactly fear that keeps them from drawing on me. Let us say it is a matter of mathematics, and a problem none of them has succeeded in solving with any degree of comfort in the result. It is: how many of them would die before I did?

"You can appreciate, my friend, the quandary in which this places them, and also the disagreeable realization that bullets are no respecters of persons, nor am I. The several out there who might draw know that I know who they are. The result is that they know they would be first to die."

Childe looked at Tack thoughtfully. "I heard you ask about a riding job as I came in. You look like an honest man, and there is no place here for such."

Gentry hunted for the right words, then he said, "This country looks like it was settled by honest men."

Anson Childe studied his glass. "Yes," he said, "but at the right moment they lacked a leader. One was too opposed to violence, another was too law abiding, and the rest lacked resolution."

If there was a friend in the community, this man was

114

it. Tack finished his drink and strode to the door. The bartender met his eyes as he glanced back.

"Keep on driftin'," the bartender said.

Tack Gentry smiled. "I like it here," he said, "and I'm stayin'!"

He swung to the saddle and turned his buckskin toward Sunbonnet Pass. He still had no idea exactly what had happened during the year of his absence, yet Childe's remark coupled with what the others had said told him a little. Apparently, some strong, resolute men had moved in and taken over, and there had been no concerted fight against them, no organization and no leadership.

Childe had said that one was opposed to violence. That would have been his Uncle John. The one who was too law abiding would be Bill London. London had always been strong for law and order, and settling things in a legal way. The others had been honest men, but small ranchers, and individually unable to oppose whatever was done to them. Yet whatever had happened, the incoming elements had apparently moved with speed and finesse.

Had it been one ranch, it would have been different. But the ranches and the town seemed completely subjugated.

The buckskin took the trail at an easy canter, skirting the long red cliff of Horse Thief Mesa and wading the creek at Gunsight. Sunbonnet Pass opened before him like a gate in the mountains. To the left, in a grove of trees, was a small adobe house and a corral.

Two horses were standing at the corral as he rode up. His eyes narrowed as he saw them. Button and Blackie! Two of his uncle's favorites and two horses he had raised from colts. He swung down and started toward them, when he saw the three people on the steps.

He turned to face them, and his heart jumped. Betty London had not changed.

Her eyes widened, and her face went dead white. "Tack!" she gasped. "Tack Gentry!"

Even as she spoke, Tack saw the sudden shock with which the two men turned to stare. "That's right, Betty," he said quietly, "I just got home."

"But—but—we heard you were dead!"

"I'm not." His eyes shifted to the two men. A thick shouldered, deep chested man with a square, swarthy face, and the lean rawboned man wearing a star. The one with the star would be Dick Olney. The other must be Van Hardin.

Tack's eyes swung to Olney. "I heard my Uncle John Gentry was killed. Did yuh investigate his death?"

Olney's eyes were careful. "Yeah," he said, "he was killed in a fair fight. Gun in his hand."

"My uncle," Tack replied, "was a Quaker. He never lifted a hand in violence in his life!"

"He was a might slow, I reckon," Olney said coolly, "but he had the gun in his hand when I found him."

"Who shot him?"

"Hombre name of Soderman. But like I say, it was a fair fight."

"Like blazes!" Tack flashed. "Yuh'll never make me believe Uncle John wore a gun! That gun was planted on him!"

"Yuh're jumpin' to conclusions," Van Hardin said smoothly. "I saw the gun myself. There were a dozen witnesses."

"Who saw the fight?" Gentry demanded.

116

"They saw the gun in his hand. In his right hand," Hardin said.

Tack laughed suddenly, harshly. "That does it! Uncle John's right hand has been useless ever since Shiloh when it was shot to pieces tryin' to get to a wounded soldier. He couldn't hold a feather in those fingers, let alone a gun!"

Hardin's face tightened, and Dick Olney's eyes shifted to Hardin's face.

"You'd be better off," Hardin said quietly, "to let sleepin' dogs lie. We ain't goin' to have yuh comin' in here stirrin' up a peaceful community."

"My Uncle John was murdered," Gentry said quietly, "I mean to see his murderer punished. That ranch belongs to me. I intend to get it back!"

Van Hardin smiled. "Evidently, yuh aren't aware of what happened here," he said quietly. "Your Uncle John was in a non-combatant outfit durin' the War, was he not? Well, while he was gone, the ranch he had claimed was abandoned. Soderman and I started to run cattle on that range and the land that was claimed by Bill London. No claim to the range was asserted by anyone. We made improvements, then durin' our temporary absence with a trail herd, John Gentry and Bill London returned and moved in. Naturally, when we returned the case was taken to court. The court ruled the ranches belonged to Soderman and myself."

"And the cattle?" Tack asked. "What of the cattle my uncle owned?"

Hardin shrugged. "The brand had been taken over by the new owners and registered in their name. As I understand it, yuh left on a trail herd immediately after yuh came back to Texas. My claim was originally asserted during yore Uncle's absence. I could," he

117

smiled, "lay claim to the money yuh got from that trail herd. Where is it?"

"Suppose yuh find out?" Tex replied. "I'm goin' to tell yuh one thing: I'm goin' to find who murdered my uncle, if it was Soderman or not. I'm also goin' to fight yuh in court. Now, if yuh'll excuse me," he turned his eyes to Betty who had stood wide-eyed and silent, "I'd like to talk to Bill London."

"He can't see yuh," Hardin said. "He's asleep."

Gentry's eyes hardened. "You runnin' this place too?"

"Betty London is going to work for me," Hardin replied. "We may be married later, so in a sense, I'm speaking for her."

"Is that right?" Tack demanded, his eyes meeting Betty's.

Her face was miserable. "I'm afraid it is, Tack."

"You've forgotten your promise then?" he demanded.

"Things—things changed, Tack," she faltered. "I—I can't talk about it."

"I reckon, Gentry," Olney interrupted, "it's time yuh rode on. There's nothin' in this neck of the woods for yuh. Yuh've played out yore hand here. Ride on, and you'll save yourself a lot of trouble. They're hirin' hands over on the Pecos."

"I'm stayin'," Gentry said flatly.

"Remember," Olney warned, "I'm the sheriff. At the first sign of trouble, I'll come lookin' for yuh."

CHAPTER TWO

The Fight Begins

Gentry swung into the saddle, his eyes shifted to Betty's face and for an instant, she seemed about to speak, then he turned and rode away. He did not look back. It was not until after he was gone that he remembered Button and Blackie.

To think they were in the possession of Hardin and Olney! The twin blacks he had reared and worked with, training them to do tricks, teaching them all the lore of the cow country horses and much more.

The picture was clear now. In the year in which he had been gone these men had come in, asserted their claims, taken them to carpetbag courts, and made them stick. Backing their legal claims with guns, they had taken over the country with speed and finesse. At every turn, he was blocked. Betty had turned against him. Bill London was either a prisoner in his own house, or something was wrong. Olney was sheriff, and probably they had their own judge.

119

He could quit. He could pull out and go on to the Pecos. It would be the easiest way. It was even what Uncle John might have wished him to do, for John Gentry was a peace loving man. Tack Gentry was of another breed. His father had been killed fighting Comanches, and Tack had gone to war when a mere boy. Uncle John had found a place for himself in a non-combatant outfit, but Tack had fought long and well.

His ride north with the trail herd had been rought and bloody. Twice they had fought off Indians, once they had mixed it with rustlers. In Ellsworth, a gunman named Paris had made trouble that ended with Paris dead on the floor.

Tack had left town in a hurry, ridden to the new camp at Dodge, and then joined a trail herd headed for Wyoming. Indian fighting had been the order of the day, and once, rounding up a bunch of steers lost from the herd in a stampede, Tack had run into three rustlers after the same steers.

Tack downed two of them in the subsequent battle, and then shot it out with the other in a day long rifle battle that covered a cedar and boulder strewn hillside. Finally, just before sundown, they met in hand to hand combat with bowie knives.

Tack remained long enough to see his old friend Major Powell with whom he had participated in the Wagon Box Fight, and then had wandered back to Kansas. On the Platte he joined a bunch of buffalo hunters, stayed with them a couple of months, and then trailed back to Dodge.

Sunbonnet's Longhorn Saloon was ablaze with lights when he drifted into town that night. He stopped at the livery stable and put up his horse. He had taken a roundabout route, scouting the country, so he decided that Hardin and Olney were probably already in town. By now they would know of his call at the ranch, and his meeting with Anson Childe.

He was laboring under no delusions about his future. Van Hardin would not hesitate to see him put out of the way if he attempted to regain his property. Hardin had brains, and Olney was no fool. There were things Gentry must know before anything could be done, and the one man in town who could and would know was Childe.

Leaving the livery stable he started up the street. Turning, he glanced back to see the livery man standing in the stable door. He dropped his hand quickly, but Gentry believed he had signaled someone across the street. Yet there was no one in sight, and the row of buildings seemed blank and empty.

Only three buildings were lighted. The Longhorn, a smaller, cheaper saloon, and the old general store. There was a light upstairs over the small saloon, and several lights in the annex to the Longhorn which passed as a hotel, the only one in Sunbonnet.

Tack walked along the street, his boot heels sounding loud in the still night air. Ahead of him was a space between the buildings, and when he drew abreast of it he did a quick sidestep off the street, flattening against the building.

He heard footsteps, hesitation, and then lightly running steps and suddenly a man dove around the corner, grated to a stop on the gravel, staring down the alleyway between the buildings. He did not see Tack, who was flattened in the dense shadow against the building and behind a rain barrel.

The man started forward suddenly, and Tack reached out and grabbed his ankle. Caught in midstride, the fellow plunged over on his head, then lay still. For an instant, Gentry hesitated, then struck and shielded a match with his left hand. It was the brown hatted man he had talked to on the porch of London's ranch. His head had hit a stone, and he was out cold.

Swiftly, Tack shucked the fellow's gun and emptied the shells from it, then pushed it back in his holster. A folded paper had fallen from the unconscious man's pocket, and Tack picked it up. Then moving fast, he went down the alley until he was in back of the small saloon. By the light from a back window, he read the note.

"This," he muttered, "may help!"

Come to town quick. Trouble's brewing. We can't have anything happen now. V. H.

Van Hardin. They didn't want trouble now. Why, *now?* Folding the note, he slipped it into his pocket and flattened against the side of the saloon, studied the interior. Only two men sat in the dim interior. Two men who played cards at a small table. The bartender leaned on the bar and read a newspaper. When the man turned his head, Tack recognized him.

"Red" Furness had worked for his father. He had soldiered with him. He might still be friendly. Tack lifted his knuckles and tapped lightly on the window.

At the second tap, Red looked up. Tack lighted a match and moved it past the window. Neither of the card players seemed to have noticed. Red straightened, folded his paper, then picking up a cup walked back toward the window. When he got there, he dipped the cup into the water bucket with one hand, and with the other, lifted the window a few inches.

122

"This is Tack Gentry. Where does Childe hang out?"

Red's whisper was low. "Got him an office and sleepin' room upstairs. There's a back stairway. Yuh watch yoreself."

Tack stepped away from his window and made his way to the stairway he had already glimpsed. It might be a trap, but he believed Red was loyal. Also, he was not sure the word was out to kill him. They probably merely wanted him out of the way, and hoped he could be warned to move on. The position of the Hardin group seemed secure enough.

Reaching the top of the stairs he walked along the narrow catwalk to the door. He tapped softly. After an instant, there was a voice. "What do you want?"

"This is Tack Gentry. Yuh talked to me in the saloon!" The door opened to darkness, and he stepped in. When it closed, he felt a pistol barrel against his spine.

"Hold still!" Childe warned.

Behind him a match struck, then a candle was lighted. The light still glowed in the other room, seen only by the crack under the door. Childe grinned at him. "Got to be careful," he said. "They have tried twice to drygulch me!

"I put flowers on their graves every Monday!" he smiled. "And keep an extra one dug. Ever since I had that new grave dug, I've been left alone. Somehow it seems to have a very sobering influence on the local roughs."

He sat down. "I tire quicker than I once did. So you're Gentry! Betty London told me about you. She thought you were dead. There was a rumor that you'd been killed by the Indians in Wyoming."

"No, I came out all right. What I want to know, rememberin' yuh said yuh were a lawyer, is what kind of a claim they have on my ranch?"

123

"A good one, unfortunately. While you and your uncle were gone, and most of the other men in the locality, several of these men came in and began to brand cattle. After branding a good many, they left. They returned and began working around, about the time you left, and then they ordered your uncle off.

"He wouldn't go, and they took the case to court. There were no lawyers then, and your uncle tried to handle it himself. The judge was their man, and suddenly half a dozen witnesses appeared and were sworn in. They testified that the land had been taken and held by Soderman, Olney and Hardin.

"They claimed their brands on the cattle asserted their claim to the land, to the home ranches of both London and Gentry. The free range was something else, but with the two big ranches in their hands, and the bulk of the free range lying beyond their holdings, they were in a position to freeze out the smaller ranchers. They established a squatter's right to each of the big ranches."

"Can they do that?" Tack demanded. "It doesn't seem fair!"

"The usual thing is to allow no claim unless they have occupied the land for twenty years without hindrance, but with a carpetbag court, they do about as they please. Judge Weaver is completely in Van Hardin's hands, and your Uncle John was on the losing side of this war."

"How did Uncle John get killed?" Tack asked.

Childe shrugged. "They said he called Soderman a liar and Soderman went for his gun. Your uncle had a gun on him when they found him. It was probably a cold blooded killing because Gentry planned on a trip to Austin and was going to appeal the case."

"Have yuh seen Bill London lately?"

"Only once since the accident."

"Accident?"

"Yes, London was headed for home, dozing along in the buckboard as he always did, when his team ran away with him. The buckboard overturned and London's back was injured. He can't ride any more, and can't sit up very long at a time."

"Was it really an accident?" Tack wanted to know.

Childe shrugged. "I doubt it. We couldn't prove a thing. One of the horses had a bad cut on the hip. It looked as if someone with a steel tipped bull whip had hit the animal from beside the road."

"Thorough," Tack said. "They don't miss a bet."

Childe nodded. Leaning back in his chair he put his feet on the desk. He studied Tack Gentry thoughtfully. "You know, you'll be next. They won't stand for you messing around. I think you already have them worried."

Tack explained about the man following him, then handed the note to Childe. The lawyer's eyes narrowed. "Hmm, sounds like they had some reason to soft pedal the whole thing for awhile. Maybe it's an idea for us. Maybe somebody is coming down here to look around, or maybe somebody has grown suspicious."

Tack looked at Childe thoughtfully. "What's your position in all this?"

The tall man shrugged, then laughed lightly. "I've no stake at all, Gentry. I didn't know London or your Uncle John, either. But I heard rumors, and I didn't like the attitude of the local bosses, Hardin and Olney. I'm just a burr under the saddle with which they ride this community, no more. It amuses me to needle them, and they are afraid of me."

"Got any clients?"

"Clients?" Anson Childe chuckled. "Not a one! Not likely to have any, either! In a country so throttled by one man as this is, there isn't any litigation. Nobody can win against him, and they are too busy hating Hardin to want to have trouble with each other."

"Well, then," Tack said, "yuh've got a client now. Go down to Austin, demand an investigation. Lay the facts on the table for them. Maybe yuh can't do any good, but at least yuh can stir up a lot of trouble. The main thing will be to get people talking. They evidently want quiet, so we'll give them noise.

"Find out all you can. Get some detectives started on Hardin's trail. Find out who they are, who they were, and where they came from."

Childe sat up. "I'd like it," he said ruefully, "but I don't have that kind of money." He gestured at the room. "I'm behind on my rent here. Red owns the building, so he lets me stay."

Tack grinned and unbuttoned his shirt, drawing out a money belt. "I sold some cattle up north." He counted out one thousand dollars. "Take that. Spend all or any part of it, but create a smell down there. Tell everybody about the situation here."

Childe got up, his face flushed with enthusiasm. "Man! Nothing could please me more! I'll make it hot for them! I'll—" He went into a fit of coughing, and Tack watched him gravely.

Finally Childe straightened. "You're putting your trust in a sick man, Gentry!"

"I'm putting my trust in a fighter," Tack said drily. "Yuh'll do!" He hesitated briefly. "Also, check the title on this land."

They shook hands silently, and Tack went to the door.

Softly, he opened it and stepped out into the cool night. Well, for better or worse the battle was opened. Now for the next step. He came down off the wooden stair, then walked to the street. There was no one in sight. Tack Gentry crossed the street and pushed through the swinging doors of the Longhorn.

The saloon and dance hall was crowded. A few were familiar faces, but they were sullen faces, lined and hard. The faces of bitter men, defeated, but not whipped. The others were new faces, the hard, tough faces of gun hands, the weather beaten punchers who had come in to take the new jobs. He pushed his way to the bar.

There were three bartenders now, and it wasn't until he ordered that the squat, fat man glanced down the bar and saw him. His jaw hardened and he spoke to the bartender who was getting a bottle to pour Gentry's rye.

The bartender, a lean, sallow faced man, strolled back to him. "We're not servin' you," he said, "I got my orders!"

Tack reached across the bar, his hand shooting out so fast the bartender had no chance to withdraw. Catching the man by his stiff collar, two fingers inside the collar and their knuckles jammed hard into the man's Adam's apple, he jerked him to the bar.

"Pour!" he said.

The man tried to speak, but Tack gripped harder and shoved back on the knuckles. Weakly, desperately, his face turning blue, the man poured. He slopped out twice what he got in the glass, but he poured. Then Tack shoved hard and the man brought up violently against the backbar.

Tack lifted his glass with his left hand, his eyes sweeping the crowd, all of whom had drawn back slightly. "To honest ranchers!" he said loudly and clearly and downed his drink.

A big, hard faced man shoved through the crowd. "Maybe yuh're meaning some of us ain't honest?" he suggested.

"That's right!" Tack Gentry let his voice ring out in the room, and he heard the rattle of chips cease, and the shuffling of feet died away. The crowd was listening. "That's exactly right! There were honest men here, but they were murdered or crippled. My Uncle John Gentry was murdered. They tried to make it look like a fair and square killin', they stuck a gun in his hand!"

"That's right!" A man broke in. "He had a gun! I seen it!"

Tack's eyes shifted. "What hand was it in?"

"His right hand!" the man stated positively, belligerently. "I seen it!"

"Thank you, pardner!" Tack said politely. "The gun was in John Gentry's right hand—and John Gentry's right hand had been paralyzed ever since Shiloh!"

"Huh!" The man who had seen the gun stepped back, his face whitening a little.

Somebody back in the crowd shouted out, "That's right! You're durn tootin' that's right! Never could use a rope, 'count of it!"

Tack looked around at the crowd and his eyes halted on the big man. He was going to break the power of Hardin, Olney and Soderman, and he was going to start right here.

"There's goin' to be an investigation," he said loudly, "and it'll begin down in Austin. Any of you fellers bought property from Hardin or Olney better get your money back."

"Yuh're talkin' a lot!" The big man thrust toward

128

him, his wide, heavy shoulders looking broad enough for two men. "Yuh said some of us were thieves!"

"Thieves and murderers," Tack added. "If yuh're one of the worms that crawl in Hardin's tracks, that goes for you!"

The big man lunged. "Get him, Starr!" somebody shouted loudly.

CHAPTER THREE

Flood to Freedom

Jack Gentry suddenly felt a fierce surge of pure animal joy. He stepped back and then stepped in suddenly, and his right hand swung low and hard. It caught Starr as he was coming in, and caught him in the pit of the stomach. He grunted and stopped dead in his tracks, but Tack set himself and swung wickedly with both hands. His left smashed into Starr's mouth, his right split a cut over his cheekbone. Starr staggered and fell back into the crowd. He came out of the crowd, shook his head and charged like a bull.

Tack weaved inside of the swinging fists and impaled the bigger man on a straight, hard left hand, then he crossed a wicked right to the cut cheek and gore cascaded down the man's face. Tack stepped in, smashing both hands to the man's body, then as Starr jabbed a thumb at his eye, Tack jerked his head aside and butted Starr in the face.

His nose broken, his cheek laid open to the bone, Starr staggered back, and Tack Gentry walked in, swinging with both hands. This was the beginning. This man worked for Hardin and he was going to be an example. When he left this room Starr's face was going to be a sample of the crashing of Van Hardin's power. With left and right he cut and slashed at the big man's face, and Starr, overwhelmed by the attack, helpless after that first wicked body blow, crumpled under those smashing fists. He hit the floor suddenly and lay there, moaning softly.

A man shoved through the crowd, then stopped. It was Van Hardin. He looked down at the man on the floor, then his eyes dark with hate, lifted to meet Tack Gentry's eyes.

"Lookin' for trouble, are yuh?" he said.

"Only catchin' up with some that started while I was gone, Van!" Tack said. He felt good. He was on the balls of his feet and ready. He had liked the jarring of blows, liked the feeling of combat. He was ready. "Yuh should have made sure I was dead, Hardin, before yuh tried to steal property from a kindly old man!"

"Nothing was stolen," Van Hardin said evenly, calmly. "We took only what was ours, and in a strictly legal manner."

"There will be an investigation," Gentry replied bluntly, "from Austin. Then we'll thrash the whole thing out."

Hardin's eyes sharpened and he was suddenly wary. "An investigation? What makes you think so?"

Tack was aware that Hardin was worried. "Because I'm startin' it. I'm askin' for it, and I'll get it. There was a lot you didn't know about that land yuh stole, Hardin. Yuh were like most crooks. Yuh could only see yore side of the question and it looked very simple and easy, but

131

there's always the thing yuh overlook, and *you* over-looked somethin'!"

The doors swung wide and Olney pushed into the room. He stopped, glancing from Hardin to Gentry. "What goes on here?" he demanded.

"Gentry is accusin' us of bein' thieves," Hardin said carelessly.

Olney turned and faced Tack. "He's in no position to accuse anybody of anything!" he said. "I'm arrestin' him for murder!"

There was a stir in the room, and Tack Gentry felt the sudden sickness of fear. "Murder? Are yuh crazy?" he demanded.

"I'm not, but you may be," the sheriff said. "I've just come from the office of Anson Childe. He's been murdered. Yuh were his last visitor. Yuh were observed sneaking into his place by the back stairs. I'm arresting yuh for murder."

The room was suddenly still, and Tack Gentry felt the rise of hostility toward him. Many men had admired the courage of Anson Childe, many men had been helped by him. Frightened themselves, they had enjoyed his flouting of Hardin and Olney. Now he was dead, murdered.

"Childe was my friend!" Tack protested. "He was goin' to Austin for me!"

Hardin laughed sarcastically. "Yuh mean he knew yuh had no case and refused to go, and in a fit of rage, yuh killed him. Yuh shot him."

"Yuh'll have to come with me," Olney said grimly. "Yuh'll get a fair trial."

Silently, Tack looked at him. Swiftly, thoughts raced through his mind. There was no chance for escape. The crowd was too thick, he had no idea if there was a horse out front, although there no doubt was, and his own horse was in the livery stable. Olney relieved him of his gun belt and they started toward the door. Starr, leaning against the door post, his face raw as chewed beef, glared at him evilly.

"I'll be seein' yuh!" he said softly. "Soon!"

Solderman and Hardin had fallen in around him, and behind them two of Hardin's roughs.

The jail was small, just four cells and an outer office. The door of one of the cells was opened and he was shoved inside. Hardin grinned at him. "This should settle the matter for Austin," he said. "Childe had friends down there!"

Anson Childe murdered! Tack Gentry, numbed by the blow, stared at the stone wall. He had counted on Childe, counted on his stirring up an investigation. Once started, he possessed two aces in the hole he could use to defeat Hardin in court, but it demanded a court uncontrolled by Hardin.

With Childe's death he had no friends on the outside. Betty had barely spoken to him when they met, and if she was going to work for Hardin in his dance hall, she must have changed much. Bill London was a cripple and unable to get around. Red Furness, for all his friendship, wouldn't come out in the open. Tack had no illusions about the murder. By the time the case came to trial, they would have found ample evidence. They had his guns and they could fire two or three shots from them, whatever had been used on Childe. It would be a simple thing to frame him. Hardin would have no trouble in finding witnesses.

He was standing, staring out the small window, its lower sill just on the level of his eyes, when he heard a distant rumble of thunder and a jagged streak of lightning brightened the sky, then more thunder. The rains came slowly, softly, then in steadily increasing volume. The jail was still and empty. Sounds of music and occasional shouts sounded from the Longhorn, then the roar of rain drowned them out. He threw himself down on the cot in the corner of the room, and lulled by the falling rain, was soon asleep.

A long time later, he awakened. The rain was still falling, but above it was another sound. Listening, he suddenly realized what it was. The dry wash behind the town was running, probably bank full. Lying there in the darkness, he became aware of still another sound, of the nearer rushing of water. Lifting his head, he listened. Then he got to his feet and crossed the small cell.

Water was running under the corner of the jail. There had been a good deal of rain lately, and he had noted that the barrel at the corner of the jail had been full. It was overflowing and the water had evidently washed under the corner of the building.

He walked back and sat down on the bed, and as he listened to the water, an idea came to him suddenly. Tack got up and went to the corner of the cell, and striking a match, studied the wall and floor. Both were damp. He stamped on the stone flags of the door, but they were solid. He kicked the wall. It was also solid.

How thick were those walls? Judging by what he remembered of the door, the walls were all of eight inches thick, but how about the floor? Kneeling on the floor, he struck another match, studying the mortar around the corner flagstone.

Then he felt in his pockets. There was nothing there he could use to dig that mortar. His pocket knife, his bowie knife, his keys, all were gone. Suddenly, he had an inspiration. Slipping off his wide leather belt, he began to dig at the mortar with the edge of his heavy brass belt buckle.

The mortar was damp, but he worked steadily. His hands slipped on the sweaty buckle and he skinned his fingers and knuckles on the rough stone floor, yet he persevered, scraping, scratching, digging out tiny fragments of mortar. From time to time he straightened up and stamped on the stone. It was solid as Gibraltar.

Five hours he scraped and scratched, digging until his belt buckle was no longer of use. He had scraped out almost two inches of mortar. Sweeping up the scattered grains of mortar, and digging some of the mud off his boots, he filled in the cracks as best he could. Then he walked to his bunk and sprawled out and was instantly asleep.

Early in the morning, he heard someone stirring around outside. Then Olney walked back to his cell and looked in at him. Starr followed in a few minutes carrying a plate of food and a pot of coffee. His face was badly bruised and swollen, his eyes were hot with hate. He put the food down, then walked away. Olney loitered.

"Gentry," he said suddenly, "I hate to see a good hand in this spot."

Tack looked up. "I'll bet yuh do!" he said sarcastically.

"No use talkin' that attitude," Olney protested, "after all, yuh made trouble for us. Why couldn't yuh leave well enough alone? Yuh were in the clear, yuh had a few dollars apparently, and yuh could do all right. Hardin took possession of those ranches legally. He can hold 'em, too."

"We'll see."

"No, I mean it. He can. Why don't yuh drop the whole thing?"

"Drop it?" Tack laughed. "How can I drop it? I'm in jail for murder now, and yuh know as well as I do I never killed Anson Childe. This trial will smoke the whole story out of its hole. I mean to see that it does."

Olney winced, and Tack could see he had touched a tender spot. That was what they were afraid of. They had him now, but they didn't want him, they wanted nothing so much as to be completely rid of him.

"Only make trouble for folks," Olney protested, "yuh won't get nowhere. Yuh can bet that if yuh go to trial we'll have all the evidence we need."

"Sure. I know I'll be framed."

"What can yuh expect?" Olney shrugged. "Yuh're askin' for it. Why don't yuh play smart? If yuh'd leave the country we could sort of arrange maybe to turn yuh loose."

Tack looked up at him. "Yuh mean that?" Like blazes, he told himself. I can see yuh turnin' me loose! And when I walked out yuh'd have somebody there to smoke me down, shot escaping jail. Yeah, I know. "If I thought yuh'd let me go—" he hesitated, angling to get Olney's reaction.

The sheriff put his head close to the bars. "Yuh know me, Tack," he whispered, "I don't want to see you stick yore head in a noose! Sure, yuh spoke out of turn, and yuh tried to scare up trouble for us, but if yuh'd leave, I think I could arrange it."

"Just give me the chance," Tack assured him. "Once I get out of here I'll really start movin'!" And that's no lie, he added to himself.

Olney went away, and the morning dragged slowly. The would let him go. He was praying now they would wait until the next day. Yet, even if they did permit him to escape, even if they did not have him shot as he was leaving, what could he do? Childe, his best means of assistance, was dead. At every turn he was stopped. They had the law, and they had the guns.

His talk the night before would have implanted doubts. His whipping of Starr would have pleased many, and some of them would realize that his arrest for the murder of Childe was a frame. Yet none of these people would do anything about it without leadership. None of them wanted his neck in a noose.

Olney dropped in later, and leaned close to the bars. "I'll have something arranged by tomorrow," he said.

Tack lay back on the bunk and fell asleep. All day the rain had continued without interruption except for a few minutes at a time. The hills would be soggy now, the trails bad. He could hear the wash running strongly, running like a river not thirty yards behind the jail.

Darkness fell, he ate again, and then returned to his bunk. With a good lawyer and a fair judge he could beat them in court. He had an ace in the hole that would help, and another that might do the job.

He waited until the jail was silent and he could hear the usual sounds from the Longhorn. Then he got up and walked over to the corner. All day water had been running under the corner of the jail and must have excavated a fair sized hole by now. Tack knelt down and took from his pocket the fork he had secreted after his meal.

Olney, preoccupied with plans to allow Tack Gentry to escape, and sure that Tack was accepting the plan, had paid little attention to the returned plate.

* * *

On his knees, Tack dug out the loosely filled in dust and dirt, then began digging frantically at the hole. He worked steadily for an hour, then crossed to the bucket for a drink of water and to stretch, and then he returned to work.

Another hour passed. He got up and stamped on the stone. It seemed to sink under his feet. He bent his knees and jumped, coming down hard on his heels. The stone gave way so suddenly he almost went through. He caught himself, withdrew his feet from the hole, and bent over, striking a match. It was no more than six inches to the surface of the water, and even a glance told him it must be much deeper than he had believed.

He took another look, waited an instant, then lowered his feet into the water. The current jerked at them, and then he lowered his body through the hole and let go. Instantly, he was jerked away and literally thrown downstream. He caught a quick glimpse of a light from a window, and then he was whirling over and over. He grabbed frantically, hoping to get his hands on something, but they clutched only empty air. Frantically, he fought toward where there must be a bank, realizing he was in a roaring stream all of six feet deep. He struck nothing, and was thrown, almost hurtled down stream with what seemed to be overwhelming speed. Something black loomed near him and at the same instant the water caught at him, rushing with even greater power. He grabed again at the blob of blackness and his hand caught a root.

Yet it was nothing secure, merely a huge cottonwood log rushing downstream. Working his way along it, he managed to get a leg over and crawled atop it. Fortunately, the log did not roll over.

Lying there in the blackness, he realized what must

have happened. Behind the row of buildings that fronted on the street, of which the jail was one, was a shallow, sandy ditch. At one end of it the bluff reared up. The dry wash skirted one side of the triangle formed by the bluff, and the ditch formed the other. Water flowing off the bluff and off the roofs of the buildings and from the street of the town and the rise beyond it had flooded into the ditch, washing it deeper, yet now he knew he was in the current of the wash itself, now running bank full, a raging torrent.

A brief flash of lightning revealed the stream down which he was shooting like a chip in a mill race. Below, he knew, was Cathedral Gorge, a narrow, boulder strewn gash in the mountain down which this wash would thunder like an express train. Tack had seen such logs go down it, smashing into boulders, hurled against the rocky walls, then shooting at last out into the open flat below the gorge. And he knew instantly that no living thing could hope to ride a charging log through the black, roaring depths of the gorge and come out anything but a mangled, lifeless pulp.

The log he was bestriding hit a wave and water drenched him, then the log whirled dizzily around a bend in the wash. Before him, and around another bend he could hear the roar of the gorge. The log swung, then the driving roots ripped into a heap of debris at the bend of the wash, and the log swung wickedly across the current. Scrambling like a madman, Tack fought his way toward the roots, and then even as the log ripped loose, he hurled himself at the heap of debris.

He landed in a heap of broken boughs, felt something gouge him, and then scrambling, he made the rocks and clambered up into their shelter, lying there on a flat rock, gasping for breath.

CHAPTER FOUR

Return With Death

A long time later he got up. Something was wrong with his right leg. It felt numb and sore. He crawled over the rocks and stumbled over the muddy earth toward the partial shelter of a clump of trees.

He needed shelter, and he needed a gun. Tack Gentry knew now that he was free they would scour the country for him. They might believe him dead, but they would want to be certain. What he needed now was shelter, rest, and food. He needed to examine himself to see how badly he was injured, yet where could he turn?

Betty? She was too far away and he had no horse. Red Furness? Possibly, but how much the man would or would not help he did not know. Yet thinking of Red made him think of Childe. There was a place for him. If he could only get to Childe's quarters over the saloon!

Luckily, he had landed on the same side of the wash as the town. He was stiff and sore, and his leg was paining

140

him grievously. Yet there was no time to be lost. What the hour was he had no idea, but he knew his progress would be slow, and he must be careful. The rain was pounding down, but he was so wet now that it made no difference.

How long it took him he never knew. He could have been no more than a mile from town, perhaps less, yet he walked, crawled, and pulled himself to the edge of town, then behind the buildings until he reached the dark back stairway to Anson Childe's room. Step by step he crawled up. Luckily, the door was unlocked.

Once inside, he stood there in the darkness, listening. There was no sound. This room was windowless but for one very small and tightly curtained window at the top of the wall. Tack felt for the candle, found it, and fumbled for a match. When he had the candle alight, he started pulling off his clothes.

Naked, he dried himself with a towel, avoiding the injured leg. Then he found a bottle, and poured himself a drink. He tossed it off, then sat down on the edge of the bed and looked at his leg.

It almost made him sick to look at it. Hurled against a root or something in the dark, it had torn a great, mangled wound in the calf of his leg. No artery appeared to have been injured but in places his shinbone was visible through the ripped flesh. The wound in the calf was deeper. Cleansing it as best he could, he found a white shirt belonging to Childe, and bandaged his leg.

Exhausted, he fell asleep. When, he never recalled. Only hours later he awakened suddenly to find sunlight streaming through the door into the front room. His leg was stiff and sore, and when he moved it throbbed with pain. Using a cane he found hanging in the room, he pulled himself up and staggered to the door.

The curtains in the front room were up and sunlight streamed in. The rain seemed to be gone. From where he stood he could see into the street, and almost the first person he saw was Van Hardin. He was standing in front of the Longhorn talking to Soderman and the mustached man Tack had first seen at his own ranch.

The sight reminded him, and Tack hunted around for a gun. He found a pair of beautifully matched Colts, silver plated and ivory handled. He strapped them on with their ornate belt and holsters. Then, standing in a corner, he found a riot gun and a Henry rifle. He checked the loads in all the guns, found several boxes of ammunition for each of them, and emptied a box of .45's into the pockets of a pair of Childe's pants he pulled on. Then he put a double handful of shotgun shells into the pockets of a leather jacket he found.

He sat down then, for he was weak and trembling.

His time was short. Sooner or later someone would come to this room. Someone would either think of it or someone would come to claim the room for himself. Red Furness had no idea he was there, so would probably not hesitate to let anyone come up.

He locked the door, then dug around and found a stale loaf of bread, some cheese, then lay down to rest. His leg was throbbing with pain, and he knew it needed care, and badly.

When he awakened, he studied the street from a vantage point well inside the room and to one side of the window. Several knots of men were standing around talking, more men than should have been in town at that hour. He recognized one or two of them as being old timers around. Twice he saw Olney ride by, and the sheriff was carrying a riot gun.

Starr and the mustached man were loafing in front of

the Longhorn, and two other men Tack recognized as coming from the old London ranch were there.

He ate some more bread and cheese. He was just finishing his sandwich when a buckboard turned into the street, and his heart jumped when he saw Betty London was driving. Beside her in the seat was her father, Bill, worn and old, his hair white now, but he was wearing a gun!

Something was stirring down below. It began to look as if the lid was about to blow off. Yet Tack had no idea of his own status. He was an escaped prisoner, and as such could be shot on sight legally by Olney or Starr, who seemed to be a deputy. From the wary attitude of the Van Hardin men he knew that they were disturbed by their lack of knowledge of him.

Yet the day passed without incident, and finally he returned to the bunk and lay down after checking his guns once more. The time for the payoff was near, he knew that. It could come at any moment. He was lying there thinking about that and looking up at the rough plank ceiling when he heard the steps on the stairs.

He arose so suddenly that a twinge of pain shot through the weight that had become his leg. The steps were on the front stairs, not the back. A quick glance from the window told him it was Betty London.

What did she want here?

Her hand fell on the knob and it turned. He eased off the bed and turned the key in the lock. She hesitated just an instant, and then stepped in. When their eyes met hers went wide and her face went white to the lips.

"You!" she gasped. "Oh, Tack! What have you been doing! Where have you been!"

She started toward him, but he backed up and sat down on the bed. "Wait. Do they know I'm up here?" he demanded harshly.

"No, Tack. I came up to see if some papers were here, some papers I gave to Anson Childe before he was—murdered."

"Yuh think I did that?" he demanded.

"No, of course not!" Her eyes held a question. "Tack, what's the matter? Don't you like me any more?"

"Don't I like yuh?" His lips twisted with bitterness. "Lady, yuh've got a nerve to ask that! I come back and find my girl about to go dancin' in a cheap saloon dance hall, and—"

"I needed money, Tack," Betty said quietly. "Dad needed care. We didn't have any money. Everything we had was lost when we lost the ranch. Hardin offered me the job. He said he wouldn't let anybody molest me."

"What about him?"

"I could take care of him." She looked at him, puzzled. "Tack, what's the matter? Why are you sitting down? Are you hurt?"

"My leg." He shook his head as she started forward. "Don't bother about it, there's no time. What are they saying down there? What's all the crowd in town? Give it to me, quick!"

"Some of them think you were drowned in escaping from jail. I don't think Van Hardin thinks that, nor Olney. They seem very disturbed. The crowd is in town for Childe's funeral, and because some of them think you were murdered once Olney got you in jail. Some of our friends."

"Betty!" The call came from the street below. It was Van Hardin's voice.

"Don't answer!" Tack Gentry got up. His dark green eyes were hard. "I want him to come up."

Betty waited, her eyes wide, listening. Footsteps sounded on the stairway, then the door shoved open. "Bet—" Van Hardin's voice died out and he stood there, one hand on the door knob, starring at Tack.

"Howdy, Hardin," Tack said, "I was hopin' yuh'd come."

Van Hardin said nothing. His powerful shoulders filled the open door, his eyes were set, and the shock was fading from them now.

"Got a few things to tell yuh, Hardin," Tack continued gently, "before yuh go out of this feet first I want yuh to know what a sucker yuh've been."

"A sucker I've been?" Hardin laughed. "What chance have yuh got? The street down there is full of my men. Yuh've friends there, too, but they lack leadership, they don't know what to do. My men have their orders. And then, I won't have any trouble with yuh, Gentry. Yore old friends around here told me all about yuh. Soft, like that uncle of yores."

"Ever hear of Black Jack Paris, Hardin?"

"The gunman? Of course, but what's he got to do with yuh?"

"Nothin', now. He did once, up in Ellsworth, Kansas. They dug a bed for him next mornin', Hardin. He was too slow. Yuh said I was soft? Well, maybe I was once. Maybe in spots I still am, but yuh see, since the folks around here have seen me I've been over the cattle trails, been doin' some Injun fightin' and rustler killin'. It makes a sight of change in a man, Hardin.

"That ain't what I wanted yuh to know. I wanted yuh to know what a fool yuh were, tryin' to steal this ranch.

145

Yuh see, the land in our home ranch wasn't like the rest of this land, Hardin."

"What do you mean?" Hardin demanded suspiciously.

"Why, yuh're the smart boy," Tack drawled easily, "yuh should have checked before takin' so much for granted. Yuh see, the Gentry ranch was a land grant. My grandmother, she was a Basque, see? The land came to us through her family, and the will she left was that it would belong to us as long as any of us lived, that it couldn't be sold or traded, and in case we all died, it was to go to the State of Texas!"

Van Hardin stared. "What?" he gasped. "What kind of fool deal is this yuh're givin' me?"

"Fool deal is right," Tack said quietly. "Yuh see, the State of Texas knows no Gentry would sell or trade, knowin' we couldn't, so if somebody else showed up with the land, they were bound to ask a sight of questions. Sooner or later they'd have got around to askin' yuh how come."

Hardin seemed stunned. From the street below there was a sound of horses' hooves.

Then a voice said from Tack's left, "Yuh better get out, Van. There's talkin' to be done in the street. I want Tack Gentry!"

Tack's head jerked around. It was Soderman. The short squinty eyed man was staring at him, gun in hand. He heard Hardin turn and bolt out of the room; saw resolution in Soderman's eyes. Hurling himself toward the wall, Gentry's hand flashed for his pistol.

A gun blasted in the room with a roar like a cannon and Gentry felt the angry whip of the bullet, and then he fired twice, low down.

146

Soderman fell back against the door jamb, both hands grabbing at his stomach, just below his belt buckle. "Yuh shot me!" he gasped, round eyed. "Yuh shot—me!"

"Like you did my uncle," Tack said coolly. "Only yuh had better than an even break, and he had no break at all."

Gentry could feel blood from the opened wound trickling down his leg. He glanced at Betty. "I've got to get down there," he said, "he's a slick talker."

Van Hardin was standing down in the street. Beside him was Olney and nearby was Starr. Other men, a half dozen of them, loitered nearby.

Slowly, Tack Gentry began stumping down the stair. All eyes looked up. Red Furness saw him and spoke out, "Tack, these three men are Rangers come down from Austin to make some inquiries."

Hardin pointed at Gentry. "He's wanted for murdering Anson Childe! Also, for jail breaking, and unless I'm much mistaken he has killed another man up there in Childe's office!"

The Ranger looked at him curiously, then one of them glanced at Hardin, "Yuh all the hombre what lays claim to the Gentry place?"

Hardin swallowed quickly, then his eyes shifted. "No, that was Soderman. The man who was upstairs."

Hardin looked at Tack Gentry. With the Rangers here he knew his game was played out. He smiled suddenly. "Yuh've nothin' on me at all, gents," he said coolly. "Soderman killed John Gentry and laid claim to his ranch. I don't know nothin' about it."

"Yuh engineered it!" Bill London burst out. "Same as yuh did the stealin' of my ranch!"

147

"Yuh've no proof," Hardin sneered. "Not a particle! My name is on no papers, and yuh have no evidence."

Coolly, he strode across to his black horse and swung into the saddle. He was smiling gently, but there was sneering triumph behind the smile. "Yuh've nothin' on me, not a thing!"

"Don't let him get away!" Bill London shouted. "He's the wust one of the whole kit and kaboodle of 'em!"

"But he's right!" the Ranger protested. "In all the papers we've found, there's not a single item to tie him up. If he's in it, he's been almighty smart."

"Then arrest him for horse stealin'!" Tack Gentry said. "That's my black horse he's on!"

Hardin's face went cold, then he smiled. "Why, that's crazy! That's foolish," he said, "this is my horse. I reared him from a colt. Anybody could be mistaken, 'cause one black horse is like another. My brand's on him, and yuh can all see it's an old brand."

Tack Gentry stepped out in front of the black horse. "Button!" he said sharply. "Button!"

At the familiar voice, the black horse's head jerked up. "Button!" Tack called. "Hut! Hut!"

As the name and the sharp command rolled out, Button reacted like an explosion of dynamite. He jumped straight up in the air and came down hard, then he sunfished wildly, and Van Hardin hit the dirt in a heap.

"Button!" Tack commanded. "Go get Blackie!"

Instantly, the horse wheeled and trotted to the hitching rail where Blackie stood ground hitched as Olney had left him. Button caught the reins in his teeth and led the other black horse back.

The Rangers grinned. "Reckon, Mister," he said, "yuh done proved yore case. This man's a horse thief."

Hardin climbed to his feet, his face dark with fury. "Yuh think yuh'll get away with that?" His hand flashed for his gun.

Tack Gentry had been watching him, and now his own hand moved down, then up. The two guns barked as one. A chip flew from the stair post beside Tack, but Van Hardin turned slowly and went to his knees in the dust.

At almost the same instant, a sharp voice rang out. *"Olney! Starr!"*

Olney's face went white and he wheeled, hand flashing for his gun. *"Anson Childe!"* he gasped.

Childe stood on the platform in front of his room and fired once, twice, three times. Sheriff Olney went down, coughing and muttering. Starr backed through the swinging doors of the saloon and sat down hard in the sawdust.

Tack stared at him. "What the—"

The tall young lawyer came down the steps. "Fooled them, didn't I? They tried to get me once too often. I got their man with a shotgun in the face. Then I changed clothes with him and then lit out for Austin. I came in with the Rangers, then left them on the edge of town. They told me they'd let us have it our way unless they were needed."

"Saves the State of Texas a sight of money," one of the Rangers drawled, "anyway, we been checkin' on this here Hardin. On Olney, too. That's why they wanted to keep things quiet around here. They knowed we was checkin' on 'em."

The Rangers moved in and with the help of a few of the townspeople rounded up Hardin's other followers.

Tack grinned at the lawyer. "Lived up to your name, Pardner," he said. "Yuh sure did! All yore sheep in the fold, now!"

149

"What do you mean! Lived up to my name?" Anson Childe looked around.

Gentry grinned. "And a little Childe shall lead them!" he said.

DUTCHMAN'S FLAT

The dust of Dutchman's Flat had settled in a gray film upon their faces, and Neill could see the streaks made by the sweat on their cheeks and brows and knew his own must be the same. No man of them was smiling and they rode with their rifles in their hands, six grim and purposeful men upon the trail of a single rider.

They were men shaped and tempered to the harsh ways of a harsh land, strong in their sense of justice, ruthless in their demand for punishment, relentless in pursuit. From the desert they had carved their homes, and from the desert they drew their courage and their code, and the desert knows no mercy.

"Where's he headin', you reckon?"

"Home, mostly likely. He'll need grub an' a rifle. He's been livin' on the old Sorenson place."

Kimmel spat. "He's welcome to it. That place starved

153

out four men I know of." He stared at the hoof tracks ahead. "He's got a good horse."

"Big buckskin. Reckon we'll catch him, Hardin?"

"Sure. Not this side of his place, though. There ain't no short cuts we can take to head him off and he's pointin' for home straight as a horse can travel."

"Ain't tryin' to cover his trail none."

"No use tryin'." Hardin squinted his eyes against the glare of the sun. "He knows we figure he'll head for his ranch."

"He's no tenderfoot." Kesney expressed the thought that had been dawning upon them all in the last two hours. "He knows how to save a horse, an' he knows a trail."

They rode on in near silence. Hardin scratched his unshaven jaw. The dust lifted from the hoofs of the horses as they weaved their way through the cat-claw and mesquite. It was a parched and sunbaked land, with only dancing heat waves and the blue distance of the mountains to draw them on. The trail they followed led straight as a man could ride across the country. Only at draws or nests of rocks did it swerve, where they noticed the rider always gave his horse the best of it.

No rider of the desert must see a man to know him, for it is enough to follow his trail. In these things are the ways of a man made plain, his kindness or cruelty, his ignorance or cunning, his strength and his weakness. There are indications that cannot escape a man who has followed trails, and in the two hours since they had ridden out of Freedom the six had already learned much of the man they followed. And they would learn more.

"What started it?"

The words sounded empty and alone in the vast stillness of the basin.

Hardin turned his head slightly so the words could drift back. It was the manner of a man who rides much in the wind or rain. He shifted the rifle to his left hand and wiped his sweaty right palm on his coarse pants leg.

"Some loose talk. He was in the Bon Ton buyin' grub an' such. Johnny said somethin' at which he took offense an' they had some words. Johnny was wearin' a gun, but this Lock wasn't, so he gets him a gun an' goes over to the Longhorn.

"He pushed open the door an' shoots Johnny twice through the body. In the back." Hardin spat. "He fired a third shot but that missed Johnny and busted a bottle of whisky."

There was a moment's silence while they digested this, and then Neill looked up.

"We lynchin' him for the killin' or bustin' the whisky?"

It was a good question, but drew no reply. The dignity of the five other riders was not to be touched by humor. They were riders on a mission. Neill let his eyes drift over the dusty copper of the desert. He had no liking for the idea of lynching any man, and he did not know the squatter from the Sorenson place. Living there should be punishment enough for any man. Besides—

"Who saw the shooting?" he asked.

"Nobody seen it, actually. Only he never gave Johnny a fair shake. Sam was behind the bar, but he was down to the other end and it happened too fast."

"What's his name? Somebody call him Lock?" Neill asked. There was something incongruous in lynching a man whose name you did not know. He shifted in the saddle, squinting his eyes toward the distant lakes dancing in the mirage of heat waves.

155

"What's it matter? Lock, his name is. Chat Lock."

"Funny name."

The comment drew no response. The dust was thicker now and Neill pulled his bandanna over his nose and mouth. His eyes were drawn back to the distant blue of the lakes. They were enticingly cool and beautiful, lying across the way ahead and in the basin off to the right. This was the mirage that lured many a man from his trail to pursue the always retreating shoreline of the lake. It looked like water, it really did.

Maybe there was water in the heat waves. Maybe if a man knew how he could extract it and drink. The thought drew his hand to his canteen, but he took it away without drinking. The slosh water in the canteen was no longer enticing, for it was warm, brackish, and unsatisfying.

"You know him, Kimmel?" Kesney asked. He was a wiry little man, hard as a whipstock, with bits of sharp steel for eyes and brown musclecorded hands. "I wouldn't know him if I saw him."

"Sure, I know him. Big feller, strong made, rusty-like hair an' maybe forty year old. Looks plumb salty, too, an' from what I hear he's no friendly sort of man. Squattin' on that Sorenson place looks plumb suspicious, for no man came make him a livin' on that dry-as-a-bone place. No fit place for man nor beast. Ever'body figures no honest man would squat on such a place."

It seemed a strange thing, to be searching out a man whom none of them knew. Of course, they had all known Johnny Webb. He was a handsome, popular young man, a daredevil and a hellion, but a very attractive one, and a top hand to boot. They had all known him and had all liked him. Then, one of the things that made them so sure that this had been a wrong killing, even aside from the shots in the back, was the fact that Johnny Webb had

156

been the fastest man in the Spring Valley country. Fast, and a dead shot.

Johnny had worked with all these men, and they were good men, hard men, but good. Kimmel, Hardin and Kesney had all made something of their ranches, as had the others, only somewhat less so. They had come West when the going was rough, fought Indians and rustlers, then battled drought, dust and hot, hard winds. It took a strong man to survive in this country, and they had survived. He, Neill, was the youngest of them all, and the newest in the country. He was still looked upon with some reserve. He had been here only five years.

Neill could see the tracks of the buckskin and it gave him a strange feeling to realize that the man who rode that horse would soon be dead, hanging from a noose in one of those ropes attached to a saddle horn of Hardin or Kimmel. Neill had never killed a man, nor seen one killed by another man, and the thought made him uncomfortable.

Yet Johnny was gone, and his laughter and his jokes were a thing passed. They had brightened more than one roundup, more than one bitter day of heart-breaking labor on the range. Not that he had been an angel. He had been a proper hand with a gun, and could throw one. And in his time he had had his troubles.

"He's walkin' his horse," Kesney said, "leadin' him."

"He's a heavy man," Hardin agreed, "an' he figures to give us a long chase."

"Gone lame on him maybe," Kimmel suggested.

"No, that horse isn't limpin'. This Lock is a smart one."

They had walked out of the ankledeep dust now and were crossing a parched, dry plain of crusted earth. Hardin reined in suddenly and pointed.

157

"Look there." He indicated a couple of flecks on the face of the earth crust where something had spilled. "Water splashed."

"Careless," Neill said. "He'll need that water."

"No," Kesney said. "He was pourin' water in a cloth to wipe out his horse's nostrils. Bet you a dollar."

"Sure," Hardin agreed, "that's it. Horse breathes a lot better. A man runnin' could kill a good horse on this Flat. He knows that."

They rode on, and for almost a half hour, no one spoke. Neill frowned at the sun. It had been on his left a few minutes ago, and now they rode straight into it.

"What's he doin'?" Kesney said wonderingly. "This ain't the way to his place!" The trail had turned again, and now the sun was on their right. Then it turned again, and was at their backs. Hardin was in the lead and he drew up and swore wickedly.

They ranged alongside him, and stared down into a draw that cracked the face of the desert alongside the trail they had followed. Below them was a place where a horse had stood, and across the bank something white fluttered from the parched clump of greasewood.

Kesney slid from the saddle and crossed the wash. When he had the slip of white, he stared at it, and then they heard him swear. He walked back and handed it to Hardin. They crowded near.

Neill took the slip from Hardin's fingers after he had read it. It was torn from some sort of book and the words were plain enough, scrawled with a flat rock for a rest.

That was a fair shutin anyways six aint nowhars enuf, go fetch more men. Man on the gray better titen his girth or heel have him a sorebacked hoss.

158

"Why, that . . . !" Short swore softly. "He was lyin' within fifty yards of us when he come by. Had him a rifle, too, I see it in a saddle scabbard on that buckskin in town. He could have got one of us, anyway!"

"Two or three most likely," Kimmel commented. The men stared at the paper then looked back into the wash. The sand showed a trail, but cattle had walked here, too. It would make the going a little slower.

Neill, his face flushed and his ears red, was tightening his saddle girth. The others avoided his eyes. The insult to him, even if the advice was good, was an insult to them all. Their jaws tightened. The squatter was playing Indian with them, and none of them liked it.

"Fair shootin', yeah!" Sutter exploded. "Right in the back!"

The trail led down the wash now, and it was slower going. The occasional puffs of wind they had left on the desert above were gone and the heat in the bottom of the wash was ovenlike. They rode into it, almost seeming to push their way through flames that seared. Sweat dripped into their eyes until they smarted, and trickled in tiny rivulets through their dust-caked beards, making their faces itch maddeningly.

The wash spilled out into a wide, flat bed of sand left by the rains of bygone years, and the tracks were plainer now. Neill tightened his bandanna and rode on, sodden with heat and weariness. The trail seemed deliberately to lead them into the worst regions, for now he was riding straight toward an alkali lake that loomed ahead.

At the edge of the water, the trail vanished. Lock had ridden right into the lake. They drew up and stared at it, unbelieving.

"He can't cross," Hardin stated flatly. "That's deep

out to the middle. Durned treacherous, too. A horse could get bogged down mighty easy."

They skirted the lake, taking it carefully, three going one way, and three the other. Finally, glancing back, Neill caught sight of Kesney's uplifted arm.

"They found it," he said, "let's go back." Yet as he rode he was thinking what they all knew. This was a delay, for Lock knew they would have to scout the shores both ways to find his trail, and there would be a delay while the last three rejoined the first. A small thing, but in such a chase it was important.

"Why not ride right on to the ranch?" Short suggested.

"We might," Hardin speculated. "On the other hand he might fool us an' never go nigh it. Then we could lose him."

The trail became easier, for now Lock was heading straight into the mountains.

"Where's he goin'?" Kesney demanded irritably. "This don't make sense, nohow!"

There was no reply, the horsemen stretching out in single file, riding up the draw into the mountains. Suddenly Kimmel, who was now in the lead, drew up. Before him a thread of water trickled from the rock and spilled into a basin of stones.

"Huh!" Hardin stared. "I never knowed about this spring afore. Might's well have a drink." He swung down.

They all got down and Neill rolled a smoke.

"Somebody sure fixed her up nice," he said. "That wall of stone makin' that basin ain't so old."

"No, it ain't."

Short watched them drink and grinned.

"He's a fox, right enough. He's an old *ladino*, this

one. A reg'lar mossy horn. It don't take no time for one man to drink, an' one hoss. But here we got six men an' six horses to drink an' we lose more time."

"You think he really planned it that way?" Neill was skeptical.

Hardin looked around at him. "Sure. This Lock knows his way around."

When they were riding on, Neill thought about that. Lock *was* shrewd. He was desert wise. And he was leading them a chase. If not even Hardin knew of this spring, and he had been twenty years in the Spring Valley country, then Lock must know a good deal about the country. Of course, this range of mountains was singularly desolate, and there was nothing in them to draw a man.

So they knew this about their quarry. He was a man wise in the ways of desert and trail, and one who knew the country. Also, Neill reflected, it was probable he had built that basin himself. Nobody lived over this way but Lock, for now it was not far to the Sorenson place.

Now they climbed a single horse trail across the starkly eroded foothills, sprinkled with clumps of Joshua and Spanish bayonet. It was a weird and broken land, where long fingers of black lava stretched down the hills and out into the desert as though clawing toward the alkali lake they had left behind. The trail mounted steadily and a little breeze touched their cheeks. Neill lifted his hand and wiped dust from his brow and it came away in flakes, plastered by sweat.

The trail doubled and changed, now across the rock face of the burnt red sandstone, then into the lava itself, skirting hills where the exposed ledges mounted in layers like a vast cake of many colors. Then the way dipped

161

down, and they wound among huge boulders, smooth as so many water worn pebbles. Neill sagged in the saddle, for the hours were growing long, and the trail showed no sign of ending.

"Lucky he ain't waitin' to shoot," Kimmel commented, voicing the first remark in over an hour. "He could pick us off like flies."

As if in reply to his comment, there was an angry whine above them, and then the crack of a rifle.

As one man they scattered for shelter, whipping rifles from their scabbards, for all but two had replaced them when they reached the lake. Hardin swore, and Kimmel wormed his way to a better view of the country ahead.

Short had left the saddle in hihs scramble for shelter, and his horse stood in the open, the canteen making a large lump behind the saddle. Suddenly the horse leaped to solid thud of a striking bullet, and then followed the crack of the rifle, echoing over the mountainside.

Short swore viciously. "If he killed that horse . . . !" But the horse, while shifting nervously, seemed uninjured.

"Hey!" Kesney yelled. "He shot your canteen!"

It was true enough. Water was pouring onto the ground, and swearing, Short started to get up. Sutter grabbed his arm.

"Hold it! If he could get that canteen, he could get you!"

They waited, and the trickle of water slowed, then faded to a drip. All of them stared angrily at the unrewarding rocks ahead of them. One canteen the less. Still they had all fill up at the spring and should have enough. Uncomfortably, however, they realized that the object of their chase, the man called Chat Lock, knew where he was taking them, and he had not emptied that

162

canteen by chance. Now they understood the nature of the man they followed. He did nothing without object.

Lying on the sand or rocks they waited, peering ahead.

"He's probably ridin' off now!" Sutter braked.

Nobody showed any disposition to move. The idea appealed to none of them, for the shot into the canteen showed plainly enough the man they followed was no child with a rifle. Kimmel finally put his hat on a rifle muzzle and lifted it. There was no response. Then he tried sticking it around a corner.

Nothing happened, and he withdrew it. Almost at once, a shot hit the trail not far from where the hat had been. The indication was plain. Lock was warning them not only that he was still there, but that he was not to be fooled by so obvious a trick.

They waited, and Hardin suddenly slid over a rock and began a flanking movement. He crawled, and they waited, watching his progress. The cover he had was good, and he could crawl almost to where the hidden marksman must be. Finally, he disappeared from their sight and they waited. Neill tasted the water in his canteen, and dozed.

At last they heard a long yell, and looking up, they saw Hardin standing on a rock far up the trail, waving them on. Mounting, they led Hardin's horse and rode on up the trail. He met them at the trail side, and his eyes were angry.

"Gone!" he said, thrusting out a hard palm. In it lay three brass cartridge shells. "Found 'em standing up in a line on a rock. An' look here." He pointed, and they stared down at the trail where he indicated. A neat arrow made of stones pointed down the trail ahead of them, and scratched on the face of the sand stone above it were the words: FOLLER THE SIGNS.

Kesney jerked his hat from his head and hurled it to the ground.

"Why, that dirty . . . !" He stopped, beside himself with anger. The contempt of the man they pursued was obvious. He was making fools of them, deliberately teasing them, indicating his trail as to a child or a tenderfoot.

"That ratty back-shootin' killer!" Short said. "I'll take pleasure in usin' a rope on him! Thinks he's smart!"

They started on, and the horse ahead of them left a plain trail, but a quarter of a mile further along, three dried pieces of mesquite had been laid in the trail to form another arrow.

Neill stared at it. This was becoming a personal matter now. He was deliberately playing with them, and he must know how that would set with men such as Kimmel and Hardin. It was a deliberate challenge, more, it was a sign of the utmost contempt.

The vast emptiness of the basin they skirted now was becoming lost in the misty purple light of late afternoon. On the right, the wall of the mountain grew steeper and turned a deeper red. The burnt red of the earlier hours was now a bright rust red, and here and there long fingers of quartz shot their white arrows down into the face of the cliff.

They all saw the next message, but all read and averted their eyes. It was written on a blank face of the cliff. First, there was an arrow, pointing ahead, and then the words, SHADE, SO'S YOU DON'T GET SUNSTROK.

They rode on, and for several miles as the shadows drew down, they followed the markers their quarry left at intervals along the trail. All six of the men were tired and beaten. Their horses moved slowly, and the desert air was growing chill. It had been a long chase.

Suddenly, Kimmel and Kesney, who rode side by side, reined in. A small wall or rock was across the trail, and an arrow pointed downward into a deep cleft.

"What do you think, Hardin? He could pick us off man by man."

Hardin studied the situation with misgivings, and hesitated, lighting a smoke.

"He ain't done it yet."

Neill's remark fell into the still air like a rock into a calm pool of water. As the rings of ripples spread wider into the thoughts of the other five, he waited.

Lock could have killed one or two of them, perhaps all of them by now. Why had he not? Was he waiting for darkness and an easy getaway? Or was he leading them into a trap?

"The devil with it!" Hardin exclaimed impatiently. He wheeled his horse and pistol in hand, started down into the narrow rift in the dark. One by one, they followed. The darkness closed around them, and the air was damp and chill. They rode on, and then the trail mounted steeply toward a grayness ahead of them, and they came out in a small basin. Ahead of them they heard a trickle of running water and saw the darkness of trees.

Cautiously they approached. Suddenly, they saw the light of a fire. Hardin drew up sharply and slid from his horse. The others followed. In a widening circle, they crept toward the fire. Kesney was the first to reach it, and the sound of his swearing rent the stillness and shattered it like thin glass. They swarmed in around him.

The fire was built close and beside a small running stream, and nearby was a neat pile of dry sticks. On a paper, laid out carefully on a rock, was a small mound of coffee, and another of sugar. Nobody said anything for a minute, staring at the fire and the coffee. The taunt was obvious, and they were bitter men. It was bad enough to have a stranger make such fools of them on a trail, to treat them like tenderfeet, but to prepare a camp for them. . . .

"I'll be cussed if I will!" Short said violently. "I'll go sleep on the desert first!"

"Well—" Hardin was philosophical. "Might's well make the most of it. We can't trail him at night, no way."

Kimmel had dug a coffee pot out of his pack and was getting water from the stream which flowed from a basin just above their camp. Several of the others began to dig out grub, and Kesney sat down glumly, staring into the fire. He started to pick a stick of the pile left for them, then jerked his hand as though he had seen a snake and getting up, he stalked back into the trees, and after a minute, he returned.

Sutter was looking around, and suddenly he spoke. "Boys, I know this place! Only I never knew about that crack in the wall. This here's the Mormon Well!"

Hardin sat up and looked around. "Durned if it ain't," he said. "I ain't been in here for six or seven years."

Sutter squatted on his haunches. "Look!" He was excited and eager. "Here's Mormon Well, where we are. Right over here to the northwest there's an old saw mill an' a tank just above it. I'll bet a side of beef that durned killer is holed up for the night in that sawmill!"

Kesney, who had taken most to heart the taunting of the man they pursued, was on his knees staring at the diagram drawn in the damp sand. He was nodding thoughtfully.

"He's right! He sure is. I remembered that old mill! I holed up there one time in a bad storm. Spent two days in

166

it. If that sidewinder stays there tonight, we can get him!"

As they ate, they talked over their plan. Travelling over the rugged mountains ahead of them was almost impossible in the darkness, and besides, even if Lock could go the night without stopping, his horse could not. The buckskin must have rest. Moreover, with all the time Lock had been losing along the trail, he could not be far ahead. It stood to reason that he must have planned just this, for them to stop here, and to hole up in the sawmill himself.

"We'd better surprise him," Hardin suggested. "That sawmill is heavy timber an' a man in there with a rifle an' plenty of ammunition could stand us off for a week."

"Has he got plenty?"

"Sure he has," Neill told them. "I was in the Bon Ton when he bought his stuff. He's got grub and he's got plenty of .44's. They do for either his Colt or his Winchester."

Unspoken as yet, but present in the mind of each man, was a growing respect for their quarry, a respect and an element of doubt. Would such a man as this shoot another in the back? The evidence against him was plain enough, or seemed plain enough.

Yet beyond the respect there was something else, for it was no longer simply a matter of justice to be done, but a personal thing. Each of them felt in some measure that his reputation was at stake. It had not been enough for Lock to leave an obvious trail, but he must leave markers, the sort to be used for any tenderfoot. There were men in this group who could trail a woodtick through a pine forest.

"Well," Kimmel said reluctantly, and somewhat grimly, "he left us good coffee, anyway!"

167

They tried the coffee, and agreed. Few things in this world are so comforting and so warming to the heart as hot coffee on a chilly night over a campfire when the day has been long and weary. They drank, and they relaxed. And as they relaxed, the seeds of doubt began to sprout and put forth branches of speculation.

"He could have got more'n one of us today," Sutter hazarded. "This one is brush wise."

"I'll pull that rope on him!" Short stated positively. "No man makes a fool out of me!" But in his voice there was something lacking.

"You know," Kesney suggested, "if he knows these hills like he seems to, an' if he really wanted to lose us, we'd have to burn the stump and sift the ashes before we found him!"

There was no reply. Hardin drew back and eased the leg of his pants away from the skin, for the cloth had grown too hot for comfort.

Short tossed a stick from the neat pile into the fire.

"That mill ain't so far away," he suggested, "shall we give her a try?"

"Later." Hardin leaned back against a log and yawned. "She's been a hard day."

"Both them bullets go in Johnny's back?"

The question moved among them like a ghost. Short stirred uneasily, and Kesney looked up and glared around. "Sure they did! Didn't they, Hardin?"

"Sure." He paused thoughtfully. "Well, no. One of them was under his left arm. Right between the ribs. Looked like a heart shot to me. The other one went through near his spine."

"The heck with it!" Kesney declared. "No slick, rustlin' squatter can come into this country and shoot one

168

of our boys! He was shot in the back, an' I seen both holes. Johnny got that one nigh the spine, an' he must have turned and tried to draw, then got that bullet through the heart!"

Nobody had seen it. Neill remembered that, and the thought rankled. Were they doing an injustice? He felt like a traitor at the thought, but secretly he had acquired a strong tinge of respect for the man they followed.

The fire flickered and the shadows danced a slow, rhythmic quadrille against the dark background of trees. He peeled bark from the log beside him and fed it into the fire. It caught, sparked brightly, and popped once or twice. Hardin leaned over and pushed the coffee pot nearer the coals. Kesney checked the loads in his Winchester.

"How far to that saw mill, Hardin?"

"About six miles, the way we go."

"Let's get started." Short got to his feet and brushed off the sand. "I want to get home. Got my boys buildin' fence. You either keep a close watch or they are off gal hootin' over the hills."

They tightened their saddle girths, doused the fire, and mounted up. With Hardin in the lead once more, they moved off into the darkness.

Neill brought up the rear. It was damp and chill among the cliffs, and felt like the inside of a cavern. Overhead the stars were very bright. Mary was going to be worried, for he was never home so late. Nor did he like leaving her alone. He wanted to be home, eating a warm supper and going to bed in the old four poster with the patchwork quilt Mary's grandmother made, pulled over him. What enthusiasm he had had for the chase was gone. The warm fire, the coffee, his own weariness, and the growing respect for Lock had changed him.

169

Now they all knew he was not the manner of man they had supposed. Justice can be a harsh taskmaster, but Western men know their kind, and the lines were strongly drawn. When you have slept beside a man on the trail, worked with him, and with others like him, you come to know your kind. In the trail of the man Chat Lock, each rider of the posse was seeing the sort of man he knew, the sort he could respect. The thought was nagging and unsubstantial, but each of them felt a growing doubt, even Short and Kesney who were most obdurate and resentful.

They knew how a backshooter lived and worked. He had his brand on everything he did. The mark of this man was the mark of a man who did things, who stood upon his own two feet, and who if he died, died facing his enemy. To the unknowing, such conclusions might seem doubtful, but the men of the desert knew their kind.

The mill was dark and silent, a great looming bulk beside the stream and the still pool of the mill pond. They dismounted and eased close. Then according to a prearranged plan, they scattered and surrounded it. From behind a lodgepole pine, Hardin called out.

"We're comin' in, Lock! We want you!"

The challenge was harsh and ringing. Now that the moment had come something of the old suspense returned. They listened to the water babbling as it trickled over the old dam, and then they moved. At their first step, they heard Lock's voice.

"Don't come in here, boys! I don't want to kill none of you, but you come an' I will! That was a fair shootin'! You've got no call to come after me!"

Hardin hesitated, chewing his mustache. "You shot him in the back!" he yelled.

"No such thing! He was a-facin' the bar when I come in. He seen I was heeled, an' he drawed as he turned. I beat him to it. My first shot took him in the side an' he was knocked back against the bar. My second hit him in the back an' the third missed as he was a fallin'. You hombres didn't see that right."

The sound of his voice trailed off and the water chuckled over the stones, then sighed to a murmur among the trees. The logic of Locke's statement struck them all. It *could* have been that way.

A long moment passed, and then Hardin spoke up again.

"You come in an' we'll give you a trial. Fair an' square!"

"How?" Lock's voice was a challenge. "You ain't got no witness. Neither have I. Ain't nobody to say what happened there but me, as Johnny ain't alive."

"Johnny was a mighty good man, an' he was our friend!" Short shouted. "No murderin' squatter is goin' to move into this country an' start shootin' folks up!"

There was no reply to that, and they waited, hesitating a little. Neill leaned disconsolately against the tree where he stood. After all, Lock might be telling the truth. How did they know? There was no use hanging a man unless you were sure.

"Gab!" Short's comment was explosive. "Let's move in, Hardin! Let's get him! He's lyin'! Nobody could beat Johnny, we know that!"

"Webb was a good man in his own country!" Lock shouted in reply. The momentary silence that followed held them, and then, almost as a man they began moving in. Neill did not know exactly when or why he started. Inside he felt sick and empty. He was fed up on the whole business and every instinct he had told him this man was no backshooter.

171

Carefully, they moved, for they knew this man was handy with a gun. Suddenly, Hardin's voice rang out.

"Hold it, men! Stay where you are until daybreak! Keep your eyes open an' your ears. If he gets out of here he'll be lucky, an' in the daylight we can get him, or fire the mill!"

Neill sank to a sitting position behind a log. Relief was a great warmth that swept over him. There wouldn't be any killing tonight. Not tonight, at least.

Yet as the hours passed, his ears grew more and more attuned to the darkness. A rabbit rustled, a pine cone dropped from a tree, the wind stirred high in the pine tops and the few stars winked through, lonesomely peering down upon the silent men.

With daylight they moved in and they went through the doors and up to the windows of the old mill, and it was empty and still. They stared at each other, and Short swore viciously, the sound booming in the echoing, empty room.

"Let's go down to the Sorenson place," Kimmel said. "He'll be there."

And somehow they were all very sure he would be. They knew he would be because they knew him for their kind of man. He would retreat no further than his own ranch, his own hearth. There, if they were to have him and hang him, they would have to burn him out, and men would die in the process. Yet with these men there was no fear. They felt the drive of duty, the need for maintaining some law in this lonely desert and mountain land. There was only doubt which had grown until each man was shaken with it. Even Short, whom the markers by the trail had angered, and Kesney, who was the best tracker among them, even better than Hardin, and had been irritated by it, too.

The sun was up and warming them when they rode over the brow of the hill had looked down into the parched basin where the Sorenson place lay.

But it was no parched basin. Hardin drew up so suddenly his startled horse almost reared. It was no longer the Sorenson place.

The house had been patched and rebuilt. The roof had spots of new lumber upon it, and the old pole barn had been made water tight and strong. A new corral had been built, and to the right of the house was a fenced in garden of vegetables, green and pretty after the desert of the day before.

Thoughtfully, and in a tight cavalcade, they rode down the hill. The stock they saw was fat and healthy, and the corral was filled with horses.

"Been a lot of work done here," Kimmel said. And he knew how much work it took to make such a place attractive.

"Don't look like no killer's place!" Neill burst out. Then he flushed and drew back, embarrassed by his statement. He was the youngest of these men, and the newest in the country.

No response was forthcoming. He had but stated what they all believed. There was something stable, lasting, something real and genuine in this place.

"I been waitin' for you."

The remark from behind them stiffened every spine. Chat Lock was here, behind them. And he would have a gun on them, and if one of them moved, he could die.

"My wife's down there fixin' breakfast. I told her I had some friends comin' in. A posse huntin' a killer. I've told her nothin' about this trouble. You ride down there now, you keep your guns. You eat your breakfast and then if you feel bound and determined to get somebody for a fair shootin', I'll come out with anyone of you or all of you, but I ain't goin' to hang.

"I ain't namin' no one man because I don't want to force no fight on anybody. You ride down there now."

They rode, and in the dooryard, they dismounted. Neill turned them, and for the first time he saw Chat Lock.

He was a big man, compact and strong. His rusty brown hair topped a brown, sun-hardened face but with the warmth in his eyes it was friendly sort of face. Not at all what he expected.

Hardin looked at him. "You made some changes here."

"I reckon." Lock gestured toward the well. "Dug by hand. My wife worked the windlass." He looked around at them, taking them in with one sweep of his eyes. "I've got the grandest woman in the world."

Neill felt hot tears in his eyes suddenly, and busied himself loosening his saddle girth to keep the others from seeing. That was the way he felt about Mary.

The door opened suddenly, and they turned. The sight of a woman in this desert country was enough to make any man turn. What they saw was not what they expected. She was young, perhaps in her middle twenties, and she was pretty, with brown wavy hair and gray eyes and a few freckles on her nose. "Won't you come in? Chat told me he had some friends coming for breakfast, and it isn't often we have anybody in."

Heavy footed and shamefaced they walked up on the porch. Kesney saw the care and neatness with which the hard hewn planks had been fitted. Here, too, was the same evidence of lasting, of permanence, of strength.

This was the sort of man a country needed. He thought the thought before he fixed his attention to it, and then he flushed.

Inside, the room was as neat as the girl herself. How did she get the floors so clean? Before he thought, he phrased the question. She smiled.

"Oh, that was Chat's idea! He made a frame and fastened a piece of pumice stone to a stick. It cuts into all the cracks and keeps them very clean."

The food smelled good, and when Hardin looked at his hands, Chat motioned to the door.

"There's water an' towels if you want to wash up."

Neill rolled up his sleeves and dipped his hands in the basin. The water was soft, and that was rare in this country, and the soap felt good on his hands. When he had dried his hands, he walked in. Hardin and Kesney had already seated themselves and Lock's wife was pouring coffee.

"Men," Lock said, "this is Mary. You'll have to tell her your names. I reckon I missed them."

Mary. Neill looked up. She was Mary, too. He looked down at his plate again and ate a few bites. When he looked up, she was smiling at him.

"My wife's name is Mary," he said, "she's a fine girl!"

"She would be! But why don't you bring her over? I haven't talked with a woman in so long I wouldn't know how it seemed! Chat, why haven't you invited them over?"

Chat mumbled something, and Neill stared at his coffee. The men ate in uncomfortable silence. Hardin's eyes kept shifting around the room. That pumice stone. He'd have to fix up a deal like that for Jane. She was always fussing about the work of keeping a board floor clean. That wash stand inside, too, with pipes made of hollow logs to carry the water out so she wouldn't have to be running back and forth. That was an idea, too.

They finished their meal reluctantly. One by one they trooped outside, avoiding each other's eyes. Chat Lock did not keep them waiting. He walked down among them.

"If there's to be shootin'," he said quietly, "let's get away from the house."

Hardin looked up. "Lock, was that right, what you said in the mill, Was it a fair shootin'?"

Lock nodded. "It was. Johnny Webb prodded me. I didn't want trouble, nor did I want to hide behind the fact I wasn't packin' an iron. I walked over to the saloon not aimin' for trouble. I aimed to give him a chance if he wanted it. He drawed an' I beat him. It was a fair shootin'."

"All right." Hardin nodded. "That's good enough for me. I reckon you're a different sort of man than any of us figured."

"Let's mount up," Short said, "I got fence to build."

Chat Lock put his hand on Hardin's saddle. "You folks come over some time. She gets right lonesome. I don't mind it so much, but you know how women folks are."

"Sure," Hardin said, "sure thing."

"An' you bring your Mary over," he told Neill.

Neill nodded, his throat full. As they mounted the hill, he glanced back. Mary Lock was standing in the door way, waving to them, and the sunlight was very bright in the clean swept door yard.

THE TRAIL TO

PEACH MEADOW

CANYON

I

Winter snows were melting in the forests of the Kaibab, and the red-and-orange hue of the thousand-foot Vermilion Cliffs was streaked with the dampness of melting frost. Deer were feeding in the forest glades among the stands of ponderosa and fir, and the trout were leaping in the streams. Where sunlight trailed through the webbed overhang of the leaves, the water danced and sparkled.

Five deer were feeding on the grass along a mountain stream back of Finger Butte, their coats mottled by the light and shadow of the sun shining through the trees.

A vague something moved in the woods behind them and the five-pronged buck lifted his regal head and stared curiously about. He turned his nose into the wind, reading it cautiously. But his trust was betrayal, for the movement was downwind of him.

The movement came again and a young man stepped from concealment behind a huge fir not twenty feet from the nearest deer. He was straight and tall in gray, fringed buckskins, and he wore no hat. His hair was thick black and wavy, growing full over the temples, and his face was lean and brown. Smiling, he walked toward the deer with quick, lithe strides, and had taken three full steps before some tiny sound betrayed him.

The buck's head came up and swung around, and then with a startled snort it sprang away, the others following.

Mike Bastian stood grinning, his hands on his hips.

"Well, what do you think now, Roundy?" he called. "Could your Apache beat that? I could have touched him if I had jumped after him!"

Rance Roundy came out of the trees—a lean, wiry old man with a gray mustache and blue eyes that were still bright with an alert awareness.

"No, I'll be darned if any Apache ever lived as could beat that!" he chortled. "Not a mite of it! An' I never seen the day I could beat it, either. You're a caution, Mike, you sure are. I'm glad you're not sneakin' up after *my* hair!" He drew his pipe from his pocket and started stoking it with tobacco. "We're goin' back to Toadstool Canyon, Mike. Your dad sent for us."

Bastian looked up quickly. "Is there trouble, is that it?"

"No, only he wants to talk with you. Maybe—" Roundy was cautious—"he figures it's time you went out on a job. On one of those rides."

I think that's it," Mike nodded. "He said in the spring, and it's about time for the first ride. I wonder where they'll go, this time?"

"No tellin'. The deal will be well planned, though. That dad of yours would have made a fine general, Mike. He's got the head for it, he sure has. Never forgets a thing, that one."

"You've been with him a long time, haven't you?"

"Sure—since before he found you. I knowed him in Mexico in the war, and that was longer ago than I like to think. I was a boy then, my ownself.

"Son," Roundy said suddenly, "look!"

He tossed a huge pine cone into the air, a big one at least nine inches long.

With a flash of movement. Mike Bastian palmed his gun and almost as soon as it hit his hand it belched flame—and again. The second shot spattered the cone into a bunch a flying brown chips.

"Not bad!" Roundy nodded. "You still shoot too quick, though. You got to get over that, Mike. Sometimes one shot is all you'll ever get."

Side by side the two walked through the trees, the earth spongy with a thick blanket of pine needles. Roundy was not as tall as Mike, but he walked with the long, springy stride of the woodsman. He smoked in silence for some distance, and then he spoke up.

"Mike, if Ben's ready for you to go out, what will you do?"

For two steps, Bastian said nothing. Then he spoke slowly. "Why, go, I guess. What else?"

"You're sure? You're sure you want to be an outlaw?"

"That's what I was raised for, isn't it?" There was some bitterness in Mike's voice. "Somebody to take over what Ben Curry started?"

"Yeah, that's what you were raised for, all right. But this you want to remember, Mike: It's you life. Ben Curry, for all his power, can't live it for you. Moreover, times have changed since Ben and me rode into this country. It ain't free and wild like it was, because folks are comin' in, settlin' it up, makin' homes. Gettin' away won't be so easy, and your pards will change too. In fact, they have already changed.

"When Ben and me come into this country," Roundy continued, "it was every man for himself. More than one harum-scarum fella, who was otherwise all right, got himself the name of an outlaw. Nobody figured much about it them. We rustled cows, but so did half the big ranchers

181

of the West. And if a cowpoke got hard up and stopped a stage, nobody made much fuss unless he killed somebody. They figured it was just high spirits. But the last few years, it ain't like that no more. And it ain't only that the country is growin' up—it's partly Ben Curry himself."

"You mean he's grown too big?" Mike put in.

"What else? Why, your dad controls more land than there is in New York State! Got it right under his thumb! And he's feared over half the West by those who know about him, although not many do.

"Outside of this country around us nobody ain't seen Ben Curry in years, not leastwise to know him. But they've heard his name, and they know that somewhere an outlaw lives who rules a gang of almost a thousand men. That he robs and rustles where he will, and nobody has nerve enough to chase him.

"He's been smart, just plenty smart," old Roundy went on. "Men ride out and they meet at a given point. The whole job is planned in every detail, it's rehearsed, and then they pull it and scatter and meet again here. For a long time folks laid it to driftin' cowpunchers or to gangs passin' through. The way he's set up, one of the gangs he sends out might pull somethin' anywhere from San Antone to Los Angeles, or from Canada to Mexico, although usually he handles it close around.

He's been the brains, all right, but don't ever forget it was those guns of his that kept things in line. Lately, he hasn't used his guns. Kerb Perrin and Rigger Molina or some of their boys handle the discipline. He's become too big, Ben Curry has. He's like a king, and the king isn't getting any younger. How do you suppose Perrin will take it when he hears about you takin' over? You think he'll like it?"

"I don't imagine he will," Mike replied thoughtfully. "He's probably done some figuring of his own."

"You bet he has! So has Molina, and neither of them will stop short of murder to get what they want. Your dad still has them buffaloed, I think, but that isn't going to matter when the showdown comes. And I think it's here!"

"You do?" Mike said, surprise in his voice.

"Yeah, I sure do!" Roundy hesitated. "You know, Mike, I never told you this, but Ben Curry has a family."

"A family?" Despite himself, Mike Bastian was startled.

"Yes, he has a wife and two daughters, and they don't have any idea he's an outlaw. They live down near Tucson somewhere. Occasionally, they come to a ranch he owns in Red Wall Canyon, a ranch supposedly owned by Voyle Ragan. He visits them there."

"Does anybody else know this?"

"Not a soul. And don't you be tellin' anybody. You see, Ben always wanted a son, and he never had one. When your real dad was killed down in Mesilla, he took you along with him, and later he told me he was going to raise you to take over whatever he left. That was a long time ago, and since then he's spent a sight of time and money on you.

"You can track like an Apache," Roundy said looking at the tall lad beside him. "In the woods you're a ghost, and I doubt if old Ben Curry himself can throw a gun any faster than you. I'd say you could ride anything that wore hair, and what you don't know about cards, dice and roulette wheels ain't in it. You can handle a knife, fight with your fists, and you can open anything a man has ever made in the way of safes and locks. Along with that, you've had a good education, and you could take care of yourself in any company. I don't reckon there ever was a boy had the kind of education you got, and I think Ben's ready to retire."

"You mean, to join his wife and daughters?" Mike questioned.

"That's it. He's gettin' no younger, and he wants it easy-like for the last years. He was always scared of only one thing, and he had a lot of it as a youngster. That's poverty. Well, he's made his pile and now he wants to step out. Still and all, he knows he can't get out alive unless he leaves somebody behind him that's strong enough and smart enough to keep things under control. That's where you come in."

"Why don't he let Perrin have it?"

"Mike, you know Perrin. He's dangerous, that one. He's poison mean and power-crazy. He'd have gone off the deep end a long time ago if it wasn't for Ben Curry. And Rigger Molina is kill-crazy. He would have killed fifty men if it hadn't been that he knew Ben Curry would kill him when he got back. No, neither of them could handle this outfit. The whole shebang would go to pieces in ninety days if they had it."

Mike Bastian walked along in silence. There was little that was new in what Roundy was saying, but he was faintly curious as to the old man's purpose. The pair had been much together, and they knew each other as few men ever did. They had gone through the storm and hunger and thirst together, living in the desert, mountains and forest, only rarely returning to the rendezvous in Toadstool Canyon.

Roundy had a purpose in his talking and Bastian waited, listening. Yet even as he walked he was conscious of everything that went on around him. A quail had moved back into the tall grass near the stream, and there was a squirrel up ahead in the crotch of a tree. Not far back a gray wolf had crossed the path only minutes ahead of them.

It was as Roundy had said. Mike was a woodman, and the thought of taking over the outlaw band filled him with unease. Always, he had been aware this time would come, that he had been schooled for it. But before, it had seemed remote and far off. Now, suddenly, it was at hand, it was facing him.

"Mike," Roundy want on, "the country is growin' up. Last spring some of our raids raised merry hell, and some of the boys had a bad time gettin' away. When they start again, there will be trouble and lots of it. Another thing: folks don't look at an outlaw like they used to. He isn't just a wild young cowhand full of liquor, nor a fellow who needs a poke, nor somebody buildin' a spread of his own. Now, he'll be like a wolf, with every man huntin' him. Before you decide to go into this, you think it over, make up your own mind.

"You know Ben Curry, and I know you like him. Well, you should! Nevertheless, Ben had no right to raise you for an outlaw. He went his way of his own free will, and if he saw it that way, that was his own doin'. But no man has a right to say to another, 'This you must do; this you must be.' No man has a right to train another, startin' before he has a chance to make up his mind, and school him in any particular way."

The old man stopped to relight his pipe, and Mike kept silence, would let Roundy talk out what seemed to bother him.

"I think every man should have the right to decide his own destiny, in so far as he can," Roundy said, continuing his trend of thought. "That goes for you, Mike, and you've got the decision ahead of you. I don't know which you'll do. But if you decide to step out of this gang, then I don't relish bein' around when it happens, for old Ben will be fit to be tied.

"Right now, you're an honest man. You're clean as a whistle. Once you become an outlaw, a lot of things will change. You'll have to kill, too—don't forget that. It's one thing to kill in defense of your home, your family, or your country. It's another thing when you kill for money or for power."

"You think I'd have to kill Perrin and Molina?" Mike Bastian asked.

"If they didn't get you first!" Roundy spat. "Don't forget this, Mike: You're fast. You're one of the finest, and aside from Ben Curry probably the finest shot I ever saw. But that ain't shootin' at a man who's shootin at you. There's a powerful lot of difference, as you'll see!

"Take Billy the Kid, this Lincoln County gunman we hear about. Frank and George Coe, Dick Brewer, Jesse Evans—any one of them can shoot as good as him. The difference is that the part down inside of him where the nerves should be was left out. When he starts shootin' and when he's bein' shot at, he's like ice! Kerb Perrin's that way, too. Perrin's the cold type, steady as a rock. Rigger Molina's another kind of cat—he explodes all over the place. He's white-hot, but he's deadly as a rattler."

Mike was listening intently as Roundy continued his description:

"Five of them cornered him one time at a stage station out of Julesburg. When the shootin' was over, four of them were down and the fifth was holdin' a gun-shot arm. Molina, he rode off under his own power. He's a shaggy wolf, that one! Wild and uncurried and big as a bear!"

Far more than Roundy realized did Mike Bastian know the facts about Ben Curry's empire of crime. For three years now, Curry had been leading his foster son through all the intricate maze of his planning. There were spies and agents in nearly every town in the Southwest, and small groups of outlaws quartered here and there on ranches who could be called upon for help at a moment's notice.

Also, there were ranches where fresh horses could be had, and changes of clothing, and where the horses the band had ridden could be lost. At Toadstool Canyon were less than two hundred of the total number of outlaws, and many of those, while living under Curry's protection, were not of his band.

Also, the point Roundy raised had been in Mike's mind,

festering there, an abcess of doubt and dismay. The Ben Curry he knew was a huge, kindly man, even if grim and forbidding at times. He had taken the homeless boy and given him kindness and care; had, indeed, trained him as a son. Today, however, was the first inkling Mike had of the existence of that other family. Ben Curry had planed and acted with shrewdness and care.

Mike Bastian had a decision to make, a decision that would change his entire life, whether for better or worse.

Here in the country around the Vermilion Cliffs was the only world he knew. Beyond it? Well, he supposed he could punch cows. He was trained to do many things, and probably there were jobs awaiting such a man as himself.

He could become a gambler, but he had seen and known a good many gamblers and did not relish the idea. Somewhere beyond this wilderness was a larger, newer, wealthier land—a land where honest men lived and reared their families.

II

In the massive stone house at the head of Toadstool Canyon, so called because of the gigantic toadstool-like stone near the entrance, Ben Curry leaned his great weight back in his chair and stared broodingly out the door over the valley below.

His big face was blunt and unlined as rock, but the shock of hair above his leonine face was turning to gray. He was growing old. Even spring did not bring the old fire to his veins again, and it had been long since he had ridden out on one of the jobs he planned so shrewdly. It was time he quit.

Yet, for a man who had made decisions sharply and quickly, he was for the first time in his life, uncertain. For six years he had ruled supreme in this remote corner north of Colorado. For twenty years he had been an outlaw, and for fifteen of those twenty years he had ruled a gang that grew and extended its ramifications until it was an empire in itself.

Six years ago he had moved to this remote country and created the stronghold where he now lived. Across the southern limit rolled the Colorado River, with its long canyons and maze of rocky wilderness, a bar to any pursuit from the country south of the river where he operated.

Only at Lee's Ferry was there a crossing, and in a cabin nearby his men watched it, night and day. That is, it was the only crossing known to other men. There were two more crossings—one that the gang used in going to and from their raids, and the other known only to himself. It was his ace-in-the-hole, even if not his only one.

One law of the gang, never transgressed, was that there was to be no lawless activity in the Mormon country to the north of them. The Mormons and the Indians were left strickly alone, and were their friends. So were the few ranchers who lived in the area. These few traded at the stores run by the gang, and bought their supplies close to home and at cheaper prices than they could have managed elsewhere.

Ben Curry had never quite made up his mind about Kerb Perrin. He knew that Perrin was growing restive, that he was aware that Curry was aging and was eager for the power of leadership. Yet the one factor Curry couldn't be certain about was whether Perrin would stand for the taking over of the band by Mike Bastian.

Well, Mike had been well trained; it would be his problem. Ben smiled grimly. He was the old bull of the herd, and Perrin was pawing the dirt, but what would he say when a young bull stepped in? One who had not won his spurs with the gang?

That was why Curry had sent for him, for it was time Mike be groomed for leadership, time he moved out on his first job. And he had just the one. It was big, it was sudden, and it was dramatic. It would have an excellent effect on the gang if it was brought off smoothly, and he was going to let Mike plan the whole job himself.

There was a sharp knock outside, and Curry smiled a little, recognizing it.

"Come in!" he bellowed.

He watched Perrin stride into the room with his quick, nervous steps, his eyes scanning the room.

"Chief," Perrin said, "the boys are gettin' restless. It's spring, you know, and most of them are broke. Have you got anything in mind?"

"Sure, several things. But one that's good and tough! Struck me it might be a good one to break the kid in on."

"Oh?" Perrin's eyes veiled. "You mean he'll go along?"

"No, I'm going to let him run it. The whole show. It will be good for him."

Kerb Perrin absorbed that. For the first time, an element of doubt entered his mind. He had wondered before about Bastian and what his part would be in all this.

For years, Perrin had looked forward to the time when he could take over. He knew there would be trouble with Rigger Molina, but he had thought that phase of it out. He knew he could handle it. But what if Curry was planning to jump young Bastian into leadership?

Quick, hot passion surged through Perrin, and when he looked up, it was all he could do to keep his voice calm.

"You think that's wise?" he questioned. "How will the boys feel about goin' out with a green kid?"

"He knows what to do," Curry said. "They'll find he's smart as any of them, and he knows plenty. This is a big job, and a tough one."

"Who goes with him?"

"Maybe I'll let him pick them," Curry said thoughtfully. "Good practice for him."

"What's the job?" Perrin asked, voice sullen.

"The gold train!"

Perrin's fingers tightened, digging into his palms. This was the job *he* wanted! The shipment from the mines! It would be enormous, rich beyond anything they had done!

Months before, in talking of this job, he had laid out his plan for it before Curry. But it had been vetoed. He had recommended the killing of every manjack of them, and burial of them all, so the train would vanish completely.

"You sound like Molina," Curry had said chuckling. "Too bloody!"

"Dead men don't talk!" he had replied grimly.

"That will be tough for the kid," Perrin said now, slowly, "Mighty tough!"

Yet, even as he spoke he was thinking of something else. He was thinking of the effect of this upon the men of the outfit. He knew many of them liked Mike Bastian, and more than one of them had helped train him. In a way, many of the older men were as proud of Mike as if he had been their own son. If he stepped out now and brought off this job, he would acquire power and prestige in the gang equal to Perrin's own.

Fury engulfed Perrin. Curry had no right to do this to him! Sidetracking him for an untried kid. Shoving Bastian down all their throats!

Suddenly, the rage died and in its place came resolution. It was time he acted on his own. He would swing his own job, the one he had hed in mind for so long, and that would counteract the effect of the gold-train steal. Moreover, he would be throwing the challenge into Ben Curry's teeth for he would plan this job without consulting him. If there was going to be a struggle for leadership, it could begin here and now.

"He'll handle the job all right," Curry said confidently. "He has been trained, and he has the mind for it. He Plans well. I hadn't spoken of it before, but I asked his advice on a few things without letting him know why, and he always came through with the right answers,"

Kerb Perrin left the stone house filled with burning resentment but also something of triumph. At last, after years of taking orders, he was going on his own. Yet the still, small voice of fear was in him, too. What would Ben Curry do?

The thought made him quail. He had seen the cold fury of Curry when it was aroused, and he had seen him use a gun. He himself was fast, but was he as fast as Ben Curry? In his heart, he doubted it. He dismissed the thought, although storing it in his mind. Something would have to be done about Ben Curry. . .

Mike Bastian stood before Ben Curry's table and the two men stared at each other.

Ben Curry, the old outlaw chief, huge, bearlike and mighty, his eyes fierce yet glowing with a kindly light now, and something of pride, too. Facing him, tall and lithe, his shoulders broad and mighty, was Mike Bastian, child of the Frontier grown to manhood and trained in every art of the wilds, every dishonest practice in the books, every skill with weapons. Yet educated, too, a man who could conduct himself well in any company.

"You take four men and look over the ground yourself, Mike," Ben Curry was saying, "I want you to plan this one. The gold train leaves the mines on the twentieth. There will be five wagons, the gold distributed among them, although there won't be a lot of it as far as quantity is concerned. That gold train will be worth roughly five hundred thousand dollars.

"When that job is done," he continued, "I'm going to step down and leave you in command. You knew I was planning that. I'm old, and I want to live quietly for awhile, and this outfit takes a strong hand to run it. Think you can handle it?"

"I think so," Mike Bastian said softly.

"I think so, too. Watch Perrin—he's the snaky one.

Rigger is dangerous, but whatever he does will be out in the open. Not so Perrin. He's a conniver. He never got far with me because I was always one jump ahead of him. And I still am!"

The old man was silent for a few minutes, as he stared out the window.

"Mike," he said then, doubt entering his voice, "maybe I've done wrong. I meant to raise you the way I have. I ain't so sure what is right and wrong, and never was. Never gave it much thought, though.

"When I came west it was dog eat dog and your teeth had to be big. I got knocked down and kicked around some, and then I started taking big bites myself. I organized, and then I got bigger. In all these years nobody has ever touched me. If *you've* got a strong hand, you can do the same. Sometimes you'll have to buy men, sometimes you'll have to frighten them, and sometimes you'll have to kill."

He shook his head as if clearing it of memories past, then glanced up.

"Who will you take with you?" he asked "I mean, in scouting this layout."

Ben Curry waited, for it was judgment of men that Bastian would need most. It pleased him that Mike did not hesitate.

"Roundy, Doc Sawyer, Colley and Garlin."

Curry glanced at him, his eyes hard and curious. "Why?"

"Roundy has an eye for terrain like no man in this world," Mike said. "He says mine's as good, but I'll take him along to verify or correct my judgment. Doc Sawyer is completely honest. If he thinks I'm wrong, he'll say so. As for Colley and Garlin, they are two of the best men in the whole outfit. They will be pleased that I ask their help, which puts them on my side in a measure, and they can see how I work."

192

Curry nodded. "Smart—and you're right. Colley and Garlin are two of the best men, and absolutely fearless." He smiled a little. "If you have trouble with Perrin or Molina, it won't hurt to have them on your side."

Despite himself, Mike Bastian was excited. He was twenty-two years old and by Frontier standards had been a man for several years. But in all that time, aside from a few trips into the Mormon country and one to Salt Lake, he had never been out of the maze of canyons and mountains north of the Colorado.

Roundy led the way, for the trail was an old one to him. They were taking the secret route south used by the gang on their raids, and as they rode toward it, Mike stared at the country. He was always astonished by its ruggedness.

Snow still lay in some of the darker places of the forest, but as they neared the canyon the high cliffs towered even higher and the trail dipped down through a narrow gorge of rock. Countless centuries of erosion had carved the rock into grotesque figures resembling those of men and animals, colored with shades of brown, pink, gray and red, and tapering off into a pale yellow. There were shaddowed pools among the rocks, some from snow water and others from natural springs, and there were scattered clumps of oak and pinon.

In the bottom of the gorge the sun did not penetrate except at high noon, and there the trail wound along between great jumbled heaps of boulders, cracked and broken from their fall off the higher cliffs.

Mike Bastian followed Roundy, who rode humpshouldered on a ragged, gray horse that seemed as old as he himself, but as sure-footed and mountainwide. He had substituted boots for the moccasins he usually wore, although they reposed in his saddlebags, ready at hand.

Behind them rode "Doc" Sawyer, his lean saturnine

face quiet, his eyes faintly curious and interested as he scanned the massive walls of the canyon. "Tubby" Colley was short and thick-chested, and very confident—a hard jawed man who had been a first-rate ranch foreman before he shot two men and hit the outlaw trail.

"Tex" Garlin was tall, rangy and quiet. He was a Texan, and little was known of his background, although it was said he could carve a dozen notches on his guns if he wished.

Suddenly, Roundy turned the gray horse and rode abruptly at the face of the cliff, but when close up, the sand and boulders broke and a path showed along the under-scoured rock. Following this for several hundred yards they found a canyon that cut back into the cliff itself, then turned to head toward the river.

The roar of the Colorado, high with spring freshets, was loud in their ears before they reached it. Finally they came out on a sandy bank littered with driftwood.

Nearby was a small cabin and a plot of garden. The door of the house opened and a tall old man came out.

"Howdy!" he said. "I been expectin' somebody." His shrewd old eyes glanced from face to face, then hesitated at sight of Mike. "Ain't seen you before," he said pointedly.

"It's all right, Bill," Roundy said. "This is Mike Bastian."

"Ben Curry's boy?" Bill stared. "I heard a sight of you, son. I sure have! Can you shoot like they say?"

Mike flushed. "I don't know what they say," he said, grinning. "But I'll bet a lot of money I can hit the side of that mountain if it holds still."

Garlin stared at him thoughtfully, and Colley smiled a little.

"Don't take no funnin' from him," Roundy said. "That boy can shoot."

"Let's see some shootin', son," Bill suggested. "I always

did like to see a man that could shoot."

Bastian shook his head. "There's no reason for shootin'," he protested. "A man's a fool to shoot unless he's got cause. Ben Curry always taught me never to draw a gun unless I meant to use it."

"Go ahead," Colley said, "show him."

Old Bill pointed. "See that black stick end juttin' up over thar? It's about fifty maybe sixty paces. Can you hit it?"

"You mean that one?" Mike palmed his gun and fired, and the black stick pulverized.

It was a movement so smooth and practiced that no one of the men even guessed he had intended to shoot, and Garlin's jaws stopped their calm chewing and he stared with his mouth open for as long as it took to draw a breath. Then he glanced at Colby.

"Wonder what Kerb would say to that?" he said, astonished. "This kid can shoot!"

"Yeah," Colley agreed, "but the stick didn't have a gun!"

Old Bill worked the ferry out of a cave under the cliff and freighted them across the swollen river in one hair raising trip. With the river behind, they wound up through the rocks and started south.

III

The mining cowtown of Weaver was backed up near a large hill on the banks of a small creek. Colley and Garlin rode into the place at sundown, and an hour later Doc Sawyer and Roundy rode in.

Garlin and Colley were leaning on the bar having a drink, and they ignored the newcomers. Mike Bastian followed not long afterward, and walked to the bar alone.

Most of those in the saloon were Mexicans, but three tough-looking white men lounged against the bar nearby.

They glanced at Mike and his buckskins, and one of them whispered something to the others, at which they all laughed.

Doc Sawyer was sitting in a poker game, and his eyes lifted. Mike leaned nonchalantly against the bar, avoiding the stares of the three toughs who stood near him. One of them moved over closer.

"Hi, stranger!" he said, "That's a right purty suit you got. Where could I get one like it?"

Garlin looked up and his face stiffened. He nudged Colley. "Look!" Garlin said quickly. "Corbus and Fletcher! An' trouble huntin'! We'd better get into this!"

Colley shook his head. "No. Let's see what the kid does."

Mike looked around, his expression mild. "You want a suit like this?" he inquired of the stranger. His eyes were innocent, but he could see the sort of man he had to deal with. These three were tough, and dangerous. "Most any Navajo could make one for you."

"Just like that?" Corbus sneered.

He was drinking and in a nagging, quarrelsome mood. Mike looked altogether to neat for his taste.

"Sure! Just like this," Mike agreed. "But I don't know what you'd want with it though. This suit would be pretty hard for you to fill."

"Huh?" Corbus' face flamed. Then this mouth tightened. "You gettin' smart with me, kid?"

"No." Mike Bastian turned and his voice cracked like a whip in the suddenly silent room. "Neither am I being hurrahed by any lame-brained, liquor-guzzling saddle tramp! You made a remark about my suit, and I answered it. Nor, you can have a drink on me, all three of you, and I'm suggesting you drink up." His voice suddenly became soft. "I want to drink up because I want to be very, very sure we're friends, see?"

Corbus stared at Bastian, a cold hint of danger filtering

196

through the normal stubbornness of his brain . Something told him this was perilous going, yet he was stubborn, too stubborn. He smiled slowly. "Kid," he drawled, "supposin' I don't want to drink with no tenderfoot brat?"

Corbus never saw what happened. His brain warned him as Mike's left hand moved, but he never saw the right. The left stabbed his lips and the right cracked the side of his jaw, and he lifted from his feet and hit the floor on his shoulder blades, out cold.

Fletcher and the third tough stared from Corbus to Mike. Bastian was not smiling. "You boys want to drink?" he asked. "Or do we go on from here?"

Fletcher stared at him. "What if a man drawed a gun instead of usin' his fists?" he demanded.

"I'd kill him," Bastian replied quietly.

Fletcher blinked. "I reckon you would," he agreed. He turned, said, "Let's have a drink. That Boot Hill out there's already got twenty graves in it."

Garlin glanced at Colley, his eyebrows lifted. Colley shrugged.

"I wonder what Corbus will do when he gets up?" he said.

Garlin chuckled. "Nothin today. He won't be feelin' like it!"

Colley nodded. "Reckon you're right, an' I reckon the old man raised him a wildcat! I can hardly wait to see Kerb Perrin's face when we tell him."

"You reckon," Garlin asked, "that what we heard is true? That Ben Curry figures to put this youngster into his place when he steps out?"

"Yep, that's the talk," Colley answered.

"Well, maybe he's got it. We'll sure know before this trip is over."

Noise of the stagecoach rolling down the street drifted into the saloon, and Mike Bastian strolled outside and started toward the stage station. The passengers were getting down to stretch their legs and to eat. Three of them were women.

One of them noticed Mike standing there and walked toward him. She was a pale pretty girl with large gray eyes. "How much farther to Red Wall Canyon?" she inquired.

Mike Bastian stiffened. "Why, not far. That is, you'll make it by morning if you stick with the stage. There is a crosscountry way if you had you a buckboard, though."

"Could you tell us where we could hire one? My mother is not feeling well."

He stepped down off the boardwalk and headed toward the livery stable with her. As they drew alongside the stage, Mike looked up. An older woman and a girl were standing near the stage, but he was scarcely aware of anything but the girl. Her hair was blondish, but darker than the girl who walked beside him, and her eyes, too, were gray. There the resemblance ended, for where this girl was quiet and sweet, the other was vivid.

She looked at him and their eyes met. He swept off his hat. The girl beside him spoke.

"This is my mother, Mrs. Ragan, and my sister Drusilla." She looked up at him quickly. "My name is Juliana."

Mike bowed. He had eyes only for Drusilla, who was staring at him.

"I am Mike Bastian," he said.

"He said he could hire us a rig to drive across country to Red Wall Canyon," Juliana explained. "It will be quicker that way."

"Yes," Mike agreed, "much quicker. I'll see what I can do. Just where in Red Wall did you wish to go?"

"To Voyle Ragan's ranch," Drusilla said. "The V Bar."

He had turned away, but he stopped in midstride.

"Did you say . . . Voyle Ragan's?"

"Yes. Is there anything wrong?" Drusilla stared at him. "What's the matter?"

He regained his composure swiftly. "Nothing. Only, I'd heard the name and"—he smiled—"I sort of wanted to know for sure, so if I came calling."

Juliana laughed. "Why, of course! We'd be glad to see you."

He walked swiftly away. These, then were Ben Curry's daughters! That older women would be his wife! He was their foster brother, yet obviously his name had meant nothing to them. Neither, he reflected, would their names have meant anything to him nor the destination, had it not been for what Roundy had told him only the previous day.

Drusilla, her name was. His heart pounded at the memory of her, and he glanced back through the gathering dusk at the three women standing there by the stage.

Hiring the rig was a matter of minutes. He liked the look of the driver, a lean man, tall and white-haired. "No danger on that road this time of year," the driver said. "I can have them there in no time by taking the canyon road."

Drusilla was waiting for him when Mike walked back.

"Did you find one?" she asked, then listened to his explanation and thanked him.

"Would it be all right with you," Mike said, "if I call at the V Bar?"

She looked at him, her face grave, but a dancing light in her eyes. "Why, my sister invited you, did she not?"

"Yes, but I'd like you to invite me too,"

"I?"She studied him for a minute. "Of course, we'd be glad to see you. My mother likes visitors as well as Julie and I, so won't you ask her, too?"

I'll take the invitation from you and your sister as being enought." He grinned. "If I ask your mother, I might have to ask your father!"

"Father isn't with us!" she laughed. "We'll see him at Ragan's. He's a rancher somewhere way up north in the wilds. His name is Ben Ragan. Have you heard of him?"

"Seems to me I have," he admitted, "but I wouldn't

say for sure."

After they had gone Mike wandered around and stopped in the saloon, after another short talk with a man at the livery stable. Listening and asking an occasional question, he gathered the information he wanted on the gold shipment. Even as he asked the questions, it seemed somehow fantastic that he, of all people, should be planning such a thing.

Never before had he thought of it seriously, but now he did. And it was not only because the thought went against his own grain, but because he was thinking of Drusilla Ragan.

What a girl she was! He sobered suddenly. Yet, for all of that, she was the daughter of an outlaw. Did she know it? From her question, he doubted it very much.

Doc Sawyer cashed in his chips and left the poker game to join Mike at the bar.

"The twentieth, all right," he said softly. "And five of them are going to carry shotguns. There will be twelve guards in all, which looks mighty tough. The big fellow at the poker table is one of the guards, and all of them are picked men."

Staring at his drink, Mike puzzled over his problem. What Roundy had said was of course, true. This was a turning point for him. He was still an honest man, yet when he stepped over the boundary it would make a difference. It might make a lot of difference to a girl like Dru Ragan, for instance.

The fact that her father also was an outlaw would make little difference. Listening to Sawyer made him wonder. Why had such a man, brilliant, intelligent, and well educated, ever become a criminal?

Sawyer was a gambler and a very skillful one, yet he was a doctor, too, and a fine surgeon. His education was as good as study and money could make it, and it had been under his guidance that Mike Bastian has studied.

"Doc," he said suddenly, "whatever made you ride a crooked trail?"

Sawyer glanced at him suddenly, a new expression in his eyes. "What do you mean, Mike? Do you have doubts?"

"Doubts? That seems to be all I do have these last few days."

"I wondered about that," Doc said. "You have been so quiet that I never doubted but what you were perfectly willing to go on with Ben Curry's plans for you. It means power and money. Mike—all a man could want. If it is doubt about the future for outlaws that disturbs you, don't let it. From now on it will be political connections and bribes, but with the money you'll have to work with, that should be easy."

"It should be," Mike said slowly. "Only maybe—just maybe—I don't want to."

"Conscience rears its ugly head!" Sawyer smiled ironically. "Can it be that Ben Curry's instructions have fallen on fallow ground? What started this sudden feeling? The approach of the problem? Fear?" Doc had turned toward Mike and was staring at him with aroused interest. "Or," he added, "is there a woman? A girl?"

"Would that be so strange?"

"Strange? But no! I've wondered it hasn't happened before, but then you've lived like a recluse these past years. Who is she?"

"It doesn't matter, " Mike answered. "I was thinking of this before I saw her. Wondering what I should do."

"Don't ask me," Sawyer said. "I made a mess of my own life. Partly a woman and partly the desire for what I thought was easy money. Well, there's no such a thing as easy money, but I found that out too late. You make your own decision. What was it Matthew Arnold said? I think you learned the quotation."

" 'No man can save his brother's soul, or pay his brother's debt'."

"Right! So you save your own and pay your own. There's one thing to remember, Mike. No matter which way you go, there will be killing. If you take over Ben Curry's job, you'll have to kill Perrin and Molina, if you can. And you may have to kill them, and even Ben Curry, if you step out."

"Not Dad," Mike said.

"Don't be sure. It isn't only what he thinks that matters, Mike. No man is a complete ruler or dictator. His name is only a symbol. He is the mouthpiece for the wishes of his followers, and as long as he expresses those wishes, he leads them, When he fails, he falls. Ben Curry is the boss not only because he has power in him, but also because he has organization, because he has made them money, because he has offered them safety. If you left, there would can a chink in the armor. No outlaw ever trusts another outlaw who turns honest, for he always fears betrayal."

Bastian tossed off his drink. "Let's check with Roundy. He's been on the prowl.

Roundy came to them hastily. "We've got to get out of town, quick!" he said. "Ducrow and Fernandez just blew in and they are drunk and raisin' the devil. Both of them are talkin', too, and if they see us they will spill everything!"

"All right." Mike straightened. Get out horses. Get theirs, too, we'll take them with us."

Garlin and Colley had come to the bar. Garlin shook his head. "Ducrow's poison mean when he's drunk, and Fernandez sides him in everything," Garlin informed. "When Ducrow gets drunk he always pops off too much! The Boss forbade his weeks ago to come down here."

"He's a pal of Perrin's," Colley said, "so he thinks he can get away with it."

"Here they come now!" Roundy exclaimed.

"All right—drift!" Bastian ordered. "Make it quick with the horses."

IV

Saloon doors slammed open and the two men came in. One look, and Mike could see there was cause for worry. Tom Ducrow was drunk and ugly, and behind him was "Snake" Fernandez. They were an unpleasant pair, and they had made their share of trouble in Ben Curry's organization, though always protected by Perrin.

Bastian started forward, but he had scarcely taken a step when Durrow saw him.

"There he is!" he bellowed loudly. "The pet! The Boss' pet!" He stared around at the people in the barroom. "You know who this man is? He's—"

"Ducrow!" Mike snapped. "Shut up and go home. Now!"

"Look who's givin' orders!" Ducrow sneered. "Gettin' big for your britches, ain't you?"

"Your horses will be outside in a minute," Mike said. "Get on them and start back fast!"

"Suppose," Ducrow sneered, "you make me!"

Mike had been moving toward him, and now with a panther-like leap he was beside the outlaw and with a quick slash from his pistol barrel, floored him.

With an oath, Snake Fernandez reached for a gun, and Mike had no choice. He shot him in the shoulder. Fernandez staggered, the gun dropping from his fingers. Mouthing curses, he reached for his left-hand gun.

But even as he reached, Garlin—who had stayed behind when the others went for the horses—stepped up behind him. Jerking the gun from the man's holster, he spun him about and shoved him through the door.

Mike pulled the groggy Ducrow to his feet and pushed

him outside after Fernandez.

A big man got up hastily from the back of the room. Mike took one quick glimpse at the star on his chest.

"What goes on here?" the sheriff demanded.

"Nothing at all," Mike said affably. "Just a couple of the boys from our ranch feeling their oats a little. We'll take them out and off your hands."

The sheriff stared from Mike to Doc Sawyer and Colley, who had just come through the door.

"Who are you?" he demanded. "I don't believe I know you hombres."

"That's right, sir, you don't," Mike said. "We're from the Mogollons, riding back after driving some cattle through to California. It was a rough trip, and this liquor here got to a couple of the boys."

The sheriff hesitated, looking sharply form one to the other.

"*You* may be a cowhand," he said, "but *that* hombre"—he pointed to Sawyer—"looks like a gambler!"

Mike chuckled. "That's a joke on you, boy!" he said to Doc. Then he turned back to the sheriff. "He's a Doctor, sir, and quite a good one. A friend of my boss."

A gray-haired man got up and strolled alongside the sheriff. His eyes were alive with suspicion.

"From the Mogollons?" he queried. "That's where I'm from. Who did you say your boss was?"

Doc Sawyer felt his scalp tighten, but Mike smiled.

"Jack McCardle," he said, "of the Flying M. We aren't his regular hands, just a bunch passing through. Doc, here, he being an old friend of Jack's, handles the sale of the beef."

The Sheriff looked around.

"That right, Joe?" he asked the gray-haired man. "There a Flying M over there?"

"Yes, there is." Joe was obviously puzzled. "Good man, too, but I had no idea he was shipping beef!"

The sheriff studied Bastian thoughtfully. "Guess you're all right," he said finally. "But you sure don't *talk* like a cowhand."

"As a matter of fact," Mike said swallowing hard, "I was studying for the ministry, but my interests began to lead me in more profane directions, so I am afraid I backslid. It seems," he said gravely, "that a leaning toward poker isn't conductive to the correct manner in the pulpit!"

"I should say not!" the sheriff chuckled. "All right, son, you take your pardners with you, let 'em sleep it off."

Mike turned, and his men followed him. Ducrow and Fernandez had disappeared. They rode swiftly out of town and took the trail for Toadstool Canyon. It wasn't until they were several miles on the road that Sawyer glanced at Mike.

"You'll do," he said. "I was never so sure of a fight in my life!"

"That's right, Boss!" Garlin said. "I was bettin' we'd have to shoot our way out of town! You sure smooth-talked 'em. Never heard it done prettier!"

"Sure did," Colley agreed. "I don't envy you havin' Ducrow an' Fernandez for enemies though."

Kerb Perrin and Rigger Molina were both in conference with Ben Curry when Mike Bastian came up the stone steps and through the dorr. They both looked up sharply.

"Perrin," Bastian said, "what were Ducrow and Fernandez going in Weaver?"

"In Weaver?" Perrin straightened up slowly, nettled by Mike's tone, but puzzled, too.

"Yes, in Weaver! We nearly had to shhot our way out of town because of them. They were down there, drunk and talking to much. When to told them to get on their horses and go home, they made trouble."

Kerb Perrin was on dangerous ground. He well knew how harsh Ben Curry was about talkative outlaws, and while he had no idea what the two were doing in Weaver, he knew they were trouble-makers. He also knew they were supporters of his. Ben Curry knew it, and so did Rigger Molina.

"They made trouble?" Perrin questioned nor. "How?"

"Ducrow started to tell who I was."

"What happened?"

Mike was aware that Ben Curry had tipped back in his chair and was watching him with interest.

"I knocked him down with a pistol barrel," he said.

"You *what*?" Perrin stared. Ducrow was a bad man to tangle with. "What about Fernandez?"

"He tried to draw on me, and I put a bullet in his shoulder."

"You should've killed him," Molina said. "You'll have to, sooner or later."

Kerb Perrin was stumped. He had not expected this, or that Mike Bastian was capable of handling such a situation. He was suddenly aware that Doc Sawyer had come into the room.

Bastian faced Ben Curry. "We got what we went after," he said, "but another bad break like Ducrow and Fernandez, and we'd walk into a trap!"

"There won't be another!" Curry said harshly.

When Mike had gone out, Doc Sawyer looked at Ben Curry and smiled.

"You should have seen him and heard him," he said as Molina and Perrin were leaving. "It would have done your heart good! He had a run-in with Corbus and Fletcher, too. Knocked Corbus out with a punch and backed Fletcher down. Oh, he'll do, that boy of yours, he'll do! The way he talked that sheriff out of it was one of the smoothest things I've seen!"

Ben Curry nodded with satisfaction. "I knew it! I knew he had it!"

Doc Sawyer smiled, and looked up at the chief from

under his sunburned eyebrows. "He met a girl, too."

"A girl? Good for him! It's about time!"

"This was a very particular girl, Chief," Sawyer continued. "I thought you'd like to know. If I'm any judge of men, he fell for her and fell hard. And I'm not so sure it didn't happen both ways. He told me something about it, but I had already seen for myself."

Something in Sawyer's tone made Curry sit up a little.

"Who was the girl?" he demanded.

"A girl who came in on the stage." Doc spoke carefully, avoiding Curry's eyes now. "He got the girl and her family a rig to drive them out to a ranch. Out to the V Bar." Ben Curry's face went white. So Doc knew! It was in every line of him, every tone of his voice. The one thing he had tried to keep secret, the thing known only to himself and Roundy, was known to Doc! And to how many others?

"The girl's name," Doc continued, "was Drucilla Ragan. She's a beautiful girl."

"Well, I won't have it!" Curry said in a strained voice.

Doc Sawyer looked up, faintly curious. "You mean the foster son you raised isn't good enough for your daughter?"

"Don't say that word here!" Curry snapped, his face hard. "Who knows besides you?"

"Nobody of whom I am aware," Doc said with a shrug. "I only know by accident. You will remember the time you were laid up with that bullet wound. You were delirious, and that's why I took care of you myself— because you talked too much."

Doc lighted his pipe. "They made a nice-looking pair," he said. "And I think she invited him to Red Wall Canyon."

"He won't go! I won't have any of this crowd going there!"

"Chief, that boy's what you made him, but he's not an outlaw yet," Doc said, puffing contentedly on his pipe. "He could be, and he might be, but if he does, the crime will lie on your shoulders."

Curry shook himself and stared out the window.

"I said it, Chief: the boy has it in him," Sawyer went on. "You should have seen him throw that gun on Fernandez. The kid's fast as lightning! He thinks, too. If he takes over this gang, he'll run this country like you never ran it. I say, *if*."

"He'll do it," Curry said confidently, "you know he will. He always does what I tell him."

Doc chuckled. "He may, and again he may not. Mike Bastian has a mind of his own, and he's doing some thinking. He may decide he doesn't want to take over. What will you do then?"

"Nobody has ever quit this gang. Nobody ever will!"

"You'd order him killed?"

Ben Curry hesitated. This was something he had never dreamed of. Something— "He'll do what he's told!" he repeated, but he was no longer sure.

A tiny voice of doubt was arising within him, a voice that made him remember the Mike Bastian who was a quiet, determined little boy who would not cry, a boy who listened and obeyed. Yet now Curry knew and admitted it for the first time, that Mike Bastian always had a mind of his own.

Never before had the thought occurred to him that Mike might disobey, that he might refuse. And if he did, what then? It was a rule of the outlaw pack that no man could leave it and live. It was a rule essential to their security. A few had tried, and their bodies now lay in Boot Hill. But Mike, his son? No, not Mike!

Within him there was a deeper knowledge, an awreness that here his interests and those of the pack would divide. Even if he said no, they would say yes.

"Who would kill him, Chief? Kerb Perrin? Rigger Molina? You? Doc Sawyer shook his head slowly. "You *might* be able to do it, maybe one of the others, but I doubt it. You've created the man who may destroy you, Chief, unless you join him."

Long after Doc Sawyer was gone, Ben Curry sat there staring out over the shadowed valley. He was getting old. For the first time he was beginning to doubt his rightness, beginning to wonder if he had not wronged Mike Bastian.

And what of Mike and Dru, his beloved, gray-eyed daughter? The girl with dash and spirit? But why not? Slowly, he thought over Mike Bastian's life. Where was the boy wrong? Where was he unfitted for Dru? By the teachings given him on his, Curry's, own suggestion? His own order? Or was there yet time?

Ben Curry heaved himself to his feet and began to pace the carpeted floor. He would have to make up his mind, for a man's life and future lay in his hands, to make or break.

What if Dru wanted him anyway, outlaw or not? Ben Curry stopped and stared into the fireplace. If it had been Julie now, he might forbid it. But Dru? He chuckled. She would laugh at him. Dru had too much of his own nature, and she had a mind of her own.

* * * * *

Mike Bastian was restless the day after the excitement in Weaver. He rolled out of his bunk and walked out on the terrace. Only he and Doc Sawyer slept in the stone house where Ben Curry lived. Roundy was down in town with the rest of them, but tonight Mike wanted to walk, to think.

There had been a thrill of excitement in outtalking the sheriff, in facing down Fletcher, in flattening Corbus. And there had been more of it in facing Ducrow and Fernandez. Yet, was that what he wanted? Or did he want something more stable, more worthwhile? The something he might find with Drusilla Ragan?

Already, he had won a place with the gang. He knew the story would be all over the outlaw camp now.

Walking slowly down the street of the settlement, he turned at right angles and drifted down a side road. He wanted to get away from things for a little while, to think things out. He turned again and started back into the pines, and then he heard a voice coming from a near-by house. The words halted him. ". . . at Red Wall." Mike heard the ending.

Swiftly, he glided to the house and flattened against the side. Kerb Perrin was speaking:

"It's a cinch, and we'll do it on our own without anybody's say-so. There's about two thousand cattle in the herd, and I've got a buyer for them. We can hit the place just about sunup. Right now, they have only four hands on the place, but about the first of next month they will start hiring. It's now or not at all."

"How many men will we take?" That was Ducrow speaking.

"A dozen. That will keep the divvy large enough, and they can swing it. Hell, that Ragan ranch is easy! The boss won't hear about it until too late, and the chances are he will never guess it was us."

"I wouldn't want him to," Fernandez said.

"To hell with him!" Ducrow was irritated. "I'd like a crack at that Bastian again."

"Stick with me," Perrin said, "and I'll set him up for you. Curry is about to turn things over to him. Well, we'll beat him to it."

"You said there were girls?" Ducrow suggested.

"There's two white girls and a couple of Mexican girls who work there. One older woman. I want one of those girls myself—the youngest of the Ragan sisters. What happens to the others is none of my business."

Mike Bastian's hand dropped to his gun and his lips tightened. The tone of Perrin's voice filled him with fury, and Ducrow was as bad.

"What happens if Curry does find out?" Ducrow

demanded.

"What would happen?" Perrin said fiercely. "I'll kill him like I've wanted to all these years! I've hated that man like I never hated anyone in my life!"

"What about that Bastian?" Ducrow demanded.

Perrin laughed. "That's your problem! If you and Fernandez can't figure out how to handle him, then I don't know you."

"He knocked out Corbus, too," Ducrow aid. "We might get him to throw in with us, if this crowd is all afraid of old Ben Curry.

"I ain't so sure about him my ownself," said another voice, which Mike placed as belonging to an outlaw names Bayless. "He may not be so yound anymore, bet he's hell on wheels with a gun!"

"Forget him!" Perrin snapped. Then: "You three, and Clatt, Penelli, Monson, Kiefer and a few others will go with us. All good men. There's a lot of dissatisfaction, anyway. Molina wants to raid the Mormons. They've a lot of rich stock and there's no reason why we can't sell it south of the river, and the other stock north of it. We can get rich!"

V

Mike Bastian waited no longer, but eased away from the wall. He was tempted to wait for Perrin and brace him when he came out. His first thought was to go to Ben Curry, but he might betray his interest in Drusilla and the time was not yet ripe for that. What would her father say if he found the foster son he had raised to be an outlaw was in love with his daughter?

It was foolish to think of it, yet he couldn't help it. There was time between now and the twentieth for him to get back to Red Wall and see her.

A new thought occured to him. Ben Curry would know the girls and their mother were here and would be going to see them! That would be his chance to learn of Ben's secret pass to the river bank, and how he crossed the Colorado.

Recalling other trips, Bastian knew the route must be a much quicker one than any he knew of, and was probably farther west and and south, toward the canyon country. Already he was eager to see the girl again, and all he could think of was her trim figure, the laughter in her eyes, the soft curve of her lips.

There were other things to be considered. If there was as much unrest in the gang as Perrin said, things might be nearing a definite break. Certainly, outlaws were not the men to stand hitched for long, and Ben Curry had commanded them for longer than anyone would believe. Their loyalty was due partly to the returns from their ventures under his guidance, and partly to fear of his far-reaching power. But he was growing old, and there were those among them who feared he was losing his grip.

Mike felt a sudden urge to saddle his horse and be gone, to get away from all this potential cruelty, the conniving and hatred that lay dormant here, or was seething and ready to explode. He could ride out now by the Kaibab trail through the forest, skirt the mountains and find his own way through the canyon. It was a question whether he could escape, whether Ben Curry would let him go.

To run now meant to abandon all hope of seeing Dru again, and Mike knew he could not do that.

Returning to his quarters in the big stone house, he stopped in front of a mirror. With deadly, flashing speed, he began to practice quick draws of his guns. Each night he did this twenty times as swiftly as his darting hands could move.

Finally he sat down on his bed thinking. Roundy first, and today Doc Sawyer. Each seemed to be hoping he would

212

throw up the sponge and escape this outlaw life before it was too late. Doc said it was his life, but was it?

There was a light tap on the door. Gun in hand, he reached for the latch. Roundy stepped in. He glanced at the gun.

"Gettin' scary, Mike?" he queried. "Things are happenin'!"

"I know."

Mike went on to explain what he had overheard, and Roundy's face turned serious. "Mike, did you ever hear of Dave Lenaker?"

Bastian looked up. "You mean the Colorado gunman?"

"That's the one. He's headed this way. Ben Curry just got word that Lenaker's on his way to take over the Curry gang!"

"I thought he was one of Curry's ablest lieutenants?"

Roundy shrugged. "He was, Mike, but the word has gone out that the old man is losing his grip, and outlaws are quick to sense a thing like that. Lenaker never had any use for Perrin, and he's most likely afraid that Perrin will climb into the saddle. Dave Lenaker's a holy terror, too."

"Does Dad Curry know? Mike said.

"Yeah. He's some wrought up, too," Roundy answered. "He was figurin' on bein' away for a few days, one of those trips he takes to Red Wall. Now, he can't go."

Morning came cool and clear. Mike Bastian could feel disaster in the air, and he dressed hurriedly and headed for the bunkhouse. Few of the men were eating, and those few were silent. He knew they were all aware of impending change. He was finishing his coffee when Perrin came in.

Instantly, Mike was on guard. Perrin walked with a strut, and his eyes were bright and confident. He glanced at Bastian, faintly amused, and then sat down at the table and began to eat.

Roundy came in, and then Doc Sawyer. Mike dallied over his coffee and a few minutes later was rewarded by seeing Ducrow come in with Kiefer, followed in a few minutes by "Rocky" Clatt, Monson and Panelli.

Suddenly, with the cup half to his mouth, Mike recalled with a shock that this was the group Perrin planned to use on his raid on the Ragan ranch! That could mean the raid would come off today!

He looked up to see Roundy suddenly push back his chair and leave his breakfast unfinished. The old woodsman burried outside and vanished.

Mike put down his own cup and got up. Then he stopped, motionless. The hard muzzle of a gun was prodding him in the back, and a voice was saying, "Don't move!"

The voice was that of Fernandez, and Mike saw Perrin smiling.

"Sorry to surprise you, Bastian," Perrin said. "But with Lenaker on the road we had to move fast. By the time he gets here I'll be in the saddle. Some of the boys wanted to kill you, but I figured you'd be a good talkin' point with the Old Man. He'd be a hard kernel to dig out of that stone shell of his without you. But with you for an argument, he'll come out all right!"

"Have you gone crazy, Perrin? You can't get away with this!"

"I am, though. You see, Rigger Molina left this morning with ten of his boys to work a little job they heard of. In fact, they are on their way to knock over the gold train."

"The gold train?" Bastina exclaimed. "Why, that was *my* job! He doesn't even now the plan made for it. Or the information I got."

Perrrin smiled triumphantly. "I traded with him. I told him to give me a free hand here, and he could have the gold train. I neglected to tell him about the twelve guards riding with it, or the number of shotguns. In fact, I told him only five guards would be along. I think that will take care of Rigger for me."

Perrin turned abruptly. "Take his guns and tie his hands behind his back, then shove him out into the street. I want the Old Man to see him."

"What about him?" Kiefer demanded, pointing a gun at Doc Sawyer.

"Leave him alone. We many need a doctor, and he knows where his bread is buttered."

Confused and angry, Mike Bastian was shoved into the warm morning sun, then jerked around to face up the canyon toward the stone house.

Suddenly, fierce triumph came over him. Perrin would have a time getting the old man out of the place. The sunlight was shining down the road from over the house, full into their faces. The only approach to the house was up thirty steps of stone, overlooked by an upper window of the house. From that window, and the doorway, the entire settlement could be commanded by an expert rifleman.

Ben Curry had thought of everything. The front and back doors of every building in the settlement could be commanded easily from his stronghold.

Perrin crouched behind a pile of sandbags hastily thrown up near the door of the store.

"Come on down, Curry!" he shouted. "Give yourself up or we'll kill Bastian!"

There was no answer from up the hill. Mike felt cold and sick in the stomach. Wind touched his hair and blew a strand down over his face. He stared up at the stone house and could see no movement, hear no response.

"Come on out!" Perrin roared again. "We know you're there! Come out or we'll kill your son!"

Still no reply.

"He don't hear you," Clatt said. "Maybe he's still asleep. Let's rush the place."

"You rush it," Kiefer said. "Let me watch!"

Despite his helplessness, Mike felt a sudden glow of satisfaction. Old Ben Curry was a wily fighter. He knew that once he showed himself or spoke, their threat would take force. It was useless to kill Bastian unless they knew Curry was watching them.

Perrin had been so sure Curry would come out rather than sacrifice Mike, and now they were not even sure he was hearing them! Nor, Mike knew suddenly, was anybody sure Ben would come out even if they did warn him Mike would be killed.

"Come on out!" Perrin roared. "Give yourself up and we'll give you and Bastian each a horse and a half mile start! Otherwise, you both die! We've got dynamite!"

Mike chuckled. Dynamite wasn't going to do them much good. There was no way to get close to that stone house, backed up against the mountain as it was.

"Perrin," he said, "you've played the fool. Curry doesn't care whether I live or die. He won't come out of there, and there's no way you can get at him. All he's got to do is sit tight and wait until Dave Lenaker gets here. He will make a deal with Dave then, and where will you be?"

"Shut up!" Perrin bellowed. But for the first time he seemed to be aware that his plan was not working. "He'll come out, all right!"

"Let's open fire on the place," Ducrow suggested. "Or rush it like Clatt suggested!"

"Hell," Kiefer was disgusted. "Let's take what we can lay hands on and get out! There's two thousand head of cattle down in these bottoms. Rigger's gone, Lenaker ain't here yet, let's take what we can and get out."

"Take pennies when there's millions up there in that stone house?" Perrin demanded. His face swelled in anger and the veins stood out on his forehead. "That strong room has gold in it! Stacks of money! I know it's there. With all that at hand, would you run off with a few cattle?"

Kiefer was silent but unconvinced.

216

Standing in the dusty street, Mike looked up at the stone house. All the loyalty and love he felt for the old man up there in that house came back with a rush. Whatever he was, good or bad, he owed to Ben Curry. Perhaps Curry had reared him for a life of crime, for outlawry, but to Ben Curry it was not a bad life. He lived like a feudal lord, and had respect for no law he did not make himself.

Wrong he might be, but he had given the man that was Mike Bastian a start. Suddenly, Mike knew that he could never have been a outlaw, that it was not in him to steal and rob and kill. But that did not mean he could be unloyal to the old man who had reared him a given him a home when he had none.

He was suddenly, fiercely proud of the old man up there alone. Like a cornered grizzly, he would fight to the death. He, Mike Bastian, might die here in the street, but he hoped old Ben Curry would stay in his stone shell and defeat them all.

Kerb Perrin was stumped. He had made his plan quickly when he'd heard Dave Lenaker was on his way here, for he knew that if Lenaker arrived if might well turn into a bloody four-cornered fight. But with Molina out of the way, he might take over from Ben Curry before Lenaker and the men he brought with him in an ambush.

He had been sure that Ben Curry would reply, that he might give himself up, or at least show himself, and Perrin had a sniper concealed to pick him off if he moved into the open. That he would get nothing but silence, he could not believe.

Mike Bastian stood alone in the center of the street. There was simply nothing he could do. At any moment Perrin might decide to have him killed where he stood. With his hands tied behind him, he was helpless. Mike wondered what had happened to Roundy? The old mountain man had risen suddenly from the table and vanished. Could he be in league with Perrin.

That was impossible. Roundy had always been Ben Curry's friend, and had never liked anything about Kerb Perrin. "All right," Perrin said suddenly, "we'll hold Bastian. He's still a good argument. Some men will stay here, and the rest of us will make that raid on the Ragan outfit. I've an idea that when we come back. Curry will be ready to talk business."

VI

Bastian was led back from the street and thrown into a room in the rear of the store. There his feet were tied and he was left in darkness.

His mind was in a turmoil. If Perrin's men hit the ranch now they would take Drusilla and Juliana! He well knew how swiftly they would strike, and how helpless any ordinary ranch would be against them. And here he was tied hand and foot, helpless to do anything!

He heaved his body around and fought the ropes that bound him, until sweat streamed from his body. Even then, with his wrists torn by his struggles against the rawhide throngs that made him fast, he did not stop. There was nothing to aid him—no nail, no sharp corner, nothing at all.

The room was built of thin boards nailed to two-by-fours. He rolled himself around until he could get his back against the boards, trying to remember where the nails were. Bracing himself as best he could, he pushed his back back against the wall. He bumped against it until his back was sore. But with no effect.

Outside, all was still. Whether they had gone, he did not know. Yet if Perrin had gone on his raid, he would soon be leaving. However, if he, Mike, could escape and find Curry's private route across the river, he might beat them to it.

He wondered where Doc Sawyer was. Perhaps he was afraid of what Perrin might do if he tried to help. Where

218

was Roundy?

Just when he had all but given up, he had an idea—a solution, so simple that he cursed himself for not thinking of it before. Mike rolled over and got up on his knees and reached back with his bound hands for his spurs. Fortunately, he was wearing boots instead of the moccasins he wore in the woods. By wedging one spur against the other, he succeeded in holding the rowel almost immovable, and then he began to chafe the rawhide with the prongs of the rowel.

Desperately he sawed, until every muscle was crying for relief. As he stopped he heard the rattle of horses' hoofs. They were just going! Then he had a fighting chance if he could get free and get his hands on a gun!

He knew he was making headway for he could feel the notch he had already cut in the rawhide. Suddenly footsteps sounded outside. Fearful whoever was there would guess what he was doing, Mike rolled over on his side.

The door opened and Snake Fernandez came in, and in his hand he held a knife. His shoulder was bandaged crudely but tightly, and the knife was held in his left hand. He came in and closed the door.

Mike stared, horror mounting within him. Perrin was gone, and Snake Fernandez was moving toward him, smiling wickedly.

"You think you shoot Pablo Fernandez, eh?" the outlaw said, leering. "Now, we see who shoots! I am going to cut you to little pieces! I am going to cut you very slowly!"

Bastian lay on his shoulder and stared at Fernandez. There was murder in the breed's eyes, and all the Yaqui in him was coming to the fore. The man stooped over him and pricked him with the knife. Clamping his jaws, Mike held himself tense.

Rage mounted in the Yaqui. He leaned closer. "You do not jump, eh? I make you jump!"

He stabbed down hard with the knife, and Mike

whipped over on his shoulder blades and kicked out wickedly with his bound feet. The movement caught the killer by surprise. Mike's feet hit him on the knees and knocked him rolling. With a lunge. Mike rolled over and jerked at the ropes that bound him.

Something snapped, and he jerked again. Like a cat the killer was on his feet now, circling warily. Desparately, Mike pulled at the ropes, turning on his shoulders to keep his feet toward Fernandez. Suddenly, he rolled over and hurled himself at the Mexican's legs, but Fernandez jerked back and stabbed.

Mike felt a sliver of pain run along his arms, and then he rolled to his feet and jerked widly at the thongs. His hands came loose suddenly and he hurled himself at Fernandez's legs, grabbing one ankle.

Fernandez came down hard and Bastian jerked at the leg, then scrambled to get at him. One hand grasped the man's wrist, the other his throat. With all the power that was in him, Mike shut down on both hands.

Fernandez fought like an injured wildcat, but Mike's strength was too great. Gripping the throat with his left hand, Mike slammed the Mexican's head against the floor again and again, his throttling grip freezing tighter and tighter.

The outlaws face went dark with blood, and his struggles grew weaker. Mike let fo of his throat hold suddenly and slugged him three times on the chin with his fist.

Jerking the knife from the unconscious man's hand, Mike slashed at the thongs that bound his ankles. He got to his feet shakily. Glancing down at the sprawled-out Fernandez, he hesitated. The man was not wearing a gun, but must have had one. It could be outside the door. Easing to the door, Mike opened it a crack.

The street was deserted as far as he could see. His hands felt awkward from their long constraint, and he worked his fingers to loosen them up. There was no gun in sight, so he pushed the door wider. Fernandez's gun-belts hung over the chair on the end of the porch.

He had taken two steps toward them when a man stepped out of the bunkhouse. The fellow had a toothpick lifted to his lips, but when he saw Mike Bastian he let out a yelp of surprise and went for his gun.

It was scarcely fifteen paces and Mike threw the knife under-handed, pitching it point first off the palm of his hand. It flashed in the sun as the fellow's gun came up. Then Mike could see the haft protruding from the man's middle section.

The fellow screamed and, dropping the gun, clutched at the knife hilt in agony of fear. His breath came in horrid gasps which Mike could hear as he grabbed Fernandez's guns and belted them on. Then he lunged for the mess hall, where his own guns had been taken from him. Shoving open the door, he sprang inside, gun in hand.

Then he froze. Doc Sawyer was standing there smiling, and Doc had a shotgun on four of Perrin's men. He looked up with relief.

"I was hoping you would escape!" he said. "I didn't want to kill these men, and didn't know how to go about tying them up by myself."

Mike caught up his own guns, removed Fernandez's gun-belts and strapped his own on. Then he shoved the outlaw's guns inside the waist band of his pants.

"Down on the floor," he ordered. "I'll tie them, and fast!"

It was the work of only a few minutes to have the four outlaws bound hand and foot. He gathered up their guns.

"Where's Roundy?" he asked.

"I haven't seen him since he left here," Doc said. "I've been wondering."

"Let's go up to the house. We'll get Ben Curry, and then

we'll have things under control in a hurry."

Together, they went out the back door and walked swiftly down the line of buildings. Mike took off his hat and sailed it into the brush, knowing he could be seen from the stone house and hoping that Ben Curry would recognize him. Sawyer was excited, but trying to appear calm. He had been a gambler, and while handy with guns, was not a man accustomed to violence. Always before, he had been a bystander rather than an active participant.

Side by side, gambling against a shot from someone below, they went up the stone stairs.

There was no sound from within the house. They walked into the wide living room and glanced around. There was no sign of anyone. Then Mike saw a broken box of rifle shells.

He's been around here!" he said. Then he looked up and shouted, "Dad!"

A muffled cry reached them, and Mike was out of the room and up another staircase. He entered the room at the top, then froze in his tracks. Sawyer was behind him now.

This was the fortress room, a heavy-walled stone room that had water trickling from a spring in the wall of the cliff and running down a stone trough and out through a pipe. There was food stored here, and plenty of ammunition.

The door was heavy and could be locked and barred from within. The walls of this room were all of four feet thick, and nothing short of dynamite could have blasted a way in.

This was Ben Curry's last resort, and he was here, now. But he was sprawled on the floor, his face contorted with pain.

"Broke my leg!" he panted. "Too heavy! Tried to move too ... fast! Slipped on the steps, dragged myself up here!" He looked up at Mike. "Good for you, son! I was afraid

222

they had killed you. You got away by yourself?"

"Yes, Dad."

Sawyer had dropped to his knees, and now he looked up.

"This is a bad break, Mike," he said. "He won't be able to move."

"Get me on a bed where I can see out of that window." Ben Curry's strength seemed to flow back with his son's presence. "I'll stand them off. You and me, Mike, we can do it!"

"Dad," Mike said, "I can't stay. I've got to go."

Ben Curry's face went gray with shock, then slowly the blood flowed back into it. Bastian dropped down beside him.

"Dad, I know where Perrin's going. He's gone to make a raid on the Ragan ranch. He wants the cattle and the women."

The old man lunged so mightily that Sawyer cried out and tried to push him back. Before he could speak, Mike said:

"Dad, you must tell me about the secret crossing of the Colorado that you know. I must beat them to the ranch."

Ben Curry's expression changed to one of vast relief, and then quick calculation. He nodded.

"You could do it, but it'll take tall riding!" Quickly, he outlined the route, and then added, "Now listen! At the river there's an old Navajo. He keeps some horses for me, and he has six of the finest animals ever bred. You cross that river and get a horse from him. He knows all about you."

Mike got up. "Make him comfortable, Doc. Do all you can."

Sawyer stared at Mike. "What about Dave Lenaker? He'll kill us all!"

"I'll take care of Lenaker!" Curry flared. "I'm not dead by a danged sight! I'll show that renegade where he heads

223

in. The moment he comes up that street, I'm going to kill him!" He looked at Mike again. "Son, maybe I've done wrong to raise you like I have, but if you kill Kerb Perrin or Lenaker you would be doing the West a favor. If I don't get Dave Lenaker, you may have to. So remember this: *watch his left hand!*"

Mike ran down the steps and stopped in his room to grab his .44 Winchester. It was the work of a minute to throw a saddle on a horse, and then he hit the trail. Ben Curry and Doc Sawyer could, if necessary, last for days in the fortresslike room — unless, somehow, dynamite was pitched into the window. He would have to get to the Ragan ranch, and then get back here as soon as possible.

Mike Bastian left the stable and wheeled the gray he was riding into the long winding trail through the strands of ponderosa and fir. The horse was in fine fettle and ready for the trail, and he let it out. His mind was leaping over the trail, turning each bend, trying to see how it must lay.

This was all new country to him, for he was heading southwest now into the wild, unknown region toward the great canyons of the Colorado, a region he had never traversed and, except for old Ben Curry, perhaps never crossed by any white man.

How hard the trail would be on the horse, Mike could not guess, but he knew he must ride fast and keep going. His route was the shorter, but Kerb Perrin had a lead on him, and would be hurrying to make his strike and return.

Patches of snow still hid themselves around the roots of the brush and in the hollows under the end of some giant deadfall. The air was crisp and chill, but growing warmer, and by afternoon it would be hot in the sunlight. The wind of riding whipped his black hair, and he ran the horse down a long path bedded deep with pine needles, and then turned at a blazed tree and went out across the arid top of a plateau.

This was the strange land that he loved, the fiery,

land of the sun. Riding along the crest of a long ridge, he looked out over a long valley dotted with mesquite and sagebrush. Black dots of cattle grazing offered the only life beyond the lonely, lazy swing of a high-soaring buzzard.

He saw the white rock he had been told to look for, and turned the free-running horse into a cleft that led downward. They moved slowly here, for it was a steep slide down the side of the mesa and out on the long roll of the hill above the valley.

Time and time again Mike's hand patted his guns, as if to reassure himself they were there. His thoughts leaped ahead, trying to foresee what would happen. Would he reach the ranch first? Would he arrive only to find the buildings burned and the girls gone?

He knew only that he must get there first, that he must face them, and that at all costs he must kill Kerb Perrin and Ducrow. Without them the others might run, might not choose to fight it out. Mike had an idea that without Perrin, they would scatter to the four winds.

Swinging along the hillside, he took a trail that led again to a plateau top and ran off through the sage, heading for the smoky-blue distance of the canyon.

VII

Mike's mind lost track of time and distance, leaping ahead to the river and the crossing, and beyond it to Ragan's V Bar ranch. Down steep trails through the great, broken cliffs heaped high with the piled-up stone of ages. Down through the wild, weird jumble of boulders and across the flat toplands that smelled of sage and pinon, he kept the horse moving.

Then suddenly he was once more in the forest of the

Kaibab. The dark pines closed around him and he rode on in the vast stillness of virgin timber, the miles falling behind, the trail growing dim before him.

Then suddenly the forest split aside and he was on the rim of the canyon—an awful blue immensity yawning before him that made him draw the gray to a halt in gasping wonder. Far out over that vast, misty blue rose islands of red sandstone, islands that were laced and crossed by bands of purple and yellow. The sunset was gleaming on the vast plateaus and buttes and peaks with a ruddy glow, fading into the opaques of the deeper canyon.

The gray was beaten and weary, now. Mike turned the horse toward a break in the plateau and rode down it, giving the animal its head. They came out upon a narrow trail that hung above a vast gorge, its bottom lost in the darkness of gathering dusk. The gray stumbled on, seeming to know its day was almost done.

Dozing in the saddle, almost two hours later, Mike Bastian felt the horse come to a halt. He jerked his head up and opened his eyes. He could feel the dampness of the deep canyon and could hear the thundering roar of the mighty river as it charged through the rock-walled slit. In front of him was a square of light.

"Halloo, the house!" he called.

He swung down as the door opened.

"Who's there?" a voice cried out.

"Mike Bastian!" he said, moving toward the house with long, swinging strides. "For Ben Curry!"

The man backed into the house. He was an ancient Navajo, but his eyes were keen and sharp.

"I want a horse," Mike said.

"You can't cross the river tonight." The Navajo spoke English well, "It is impossible!"

"They'll be a moon later," Mike answered, "When it comes up, I'm going across."

The Indian looked at him, then shrugged.

"Then eat," he said, "you'll need it."

"There are horses?"

"Horses?" The Navajo chuckled. "The best a man ever saw! Do you suppose Ben Curry would have horses here that were not the best? But they are on the other side of the stream, and safe enough. My brother is with them."

Mike slumped into a seat. "Take care of my horse, will you? I've most killed him."

When the Indian was gone, Mike slumped over on the table, burying his head in his arms. In a moment he was asleep, dreaming wild dreams of a mad race over a strange misty-blue land with great crimson islands, riding a splendid black horse and carrying a girl in his arms. He awakened with a start. The old Indian was sitting by the fireplace, and he looked up.

"You'd better eat," he said. "The moon is rising."

They went out together walking, down the path to the water's edge. As the moon shone down into the canyon, Mike stared at the tumbling stream in consternation. Nothing living could swim in that water! It would be impossible.

"How do you cross?" he demanded. "No horse could swim that! And a boat wouldn't get fifty feet before it would be dashed to pieces!"

The Indian chuckled. "That isn't the way we cross it. You are right in saying no boat could cross here, for there is no landing over there, and the canyon is so narrow that the water piles up back of the narrows and comes down with a great rush."

Mike looked at him again. "You talk like an educated man," he said. "I don't understand."

The Navajo shrugged. "I was for ten years with a missionary, and after traveling with him as an interpreter he took me back to the States, where I stayed with him for two years. Then I lived in Sante Fe."

He was leading the way up a steep path that skirted the

cliff but was wide enough to walk comfortably. Opposite them, the rock wall of the canyon lifted and the waters of the tumbling river roared down through the narrow chasm.

"Ben Curry does things well, as you shall see," the guide said. "It took him two years of effort to get this bridge built."

Mike stared. "Across there?"

"Yes. A bridge for a man with courage. It is a rope bridge, made fast to iron rings sunk in the rock."

Mike Bastian halted on the rocky ledge at the end of the trail and looked out across the gorge. In the pale moonlight he could see two slim threads trailing across the canyon high above the tumbling water. Just two ropes, and one of them four feet above the other.

"You mean," he said, "that Ben Curry crossed on *that?*"

He did. I have seen him cross that bridge a dozen times, at least."

"Have you crossed it?"

The Navajo shrugged. "Why should I? The other side is the same as this, is it not? There is nothing over there that I want."

Mike looked at the slender strands, and then he took hold of the upper rope and tentatively put a foot on the lower one. Slowly, carefully, he eased out above the raging waters. One slip and he would be gone, for no man could hope to live in those angry flood waters. He slid his foot along, then the other, advancing his handholds as he moved. Little by little, he worked his way across the canyon.

He was trembling when he got his feet in the rocky cavern on the opposite side, and so relieved to be safely across that he scarcely was aware of the old Indian who sat there awaiting him.

The Navajo got up, and without a word started down

the trail. He quickly led Mike to a cabin built in the opening of a dry, branch canyon, and tethered before the door of the cabin was a large bay stallion.

Waving at the Indian, Mike swung into the saddle and the bay turned, taking to the trail as if eager to be off.

Would Perrin travel at night? Mike doubted it, but it was possible, so he kept moving himself. The trail led steadily upward, winding finally out of the canyon to the plateau.

The bay stallion seemed to know the trail; it was probable that Curry had used this horse himself. It was a splendid animal, big and very fast. Letting the horse have his head, Mike felt the animal gather his legs under him. Then he broke into a long swinging lope that literally ate up the space. How long the horse could hold the speed he did not know, but it was a good start.

It was at least a ten-hour ride to the Ragan V-Bar ranch.

The country was rugged and wild. Several times startled deer broke and ran before him, and there were many rabbits. Dawn was breaking faintly in the east now, and shortly after daybreak he stopped near a pool of melted snow water and made coffee. Then he remounted the rested stallion and raced on.

Drusilla Ragan brushed her hair thoughtfully, and then pinned it up. Outside, she could hear her mother moving about, and the Mexican girls who helped around the house whenever they were visiting. Julie was up, she knew, and had been for hours. She was outside talking to that blond cowhand from New Mexico, the one Voyle Ragan had hired to break horses.

Suddenly she heard Julie's footsteps, and then the door opened.

"Aren't you ready yet?" Julie asked. "I'm famished!"

"I'll be along in a minute." Then as Julie turned to go. "What did you think of him, Julie? That cowboy who got the buckboard for us? Wasn't he the handsomest thing?"

"Oh, you mean that Mike Bastian?" Julie said. "I was wondering why you were mooning around in here. Usually you're the first one up. Yes, I expect he is good looking. But did you see the way he looked when you mentioned Uncle Voyle? He acted so strange!"

"I wonder if Uncle Voyle knows anything about him? Let's ask!"

"You ask," Julie replied, laughing. "He's *your* problem!"

Voyle Ragan was a tall man, but lean and without Ben Curry's weight. He was already seated at the table when they came in, and Dru was no sooner in her seat than she put her question. Voyle's face became a mask.

"Mike Bastian?" he said thoughtfully. "I don't know. Where'd you meet him?"

The girls explained, and he nodded.

"In Weaver?" Voyle Ragan knew about the gold train, and his eyes narrowed. "I think I know who he is, but I never saw him that I heard of. You probably won't see him again, because most of those riders from up in the Strip stay there most of the time. They are a wild bunch."

"On the way down here," Julie said, "the man who drove was telling us that outlaws live up there."

"Could be. It's wild enough." Voyle Ragan lifted his head, listening. For a moment he had believed he heard horses. But it was too soon for Ben to be coming. If anyone else came, he would have to get rid of them, and quickly.

He heard it again, and then saw the cavalcade of horsemen riding into the yard. Voyle came to his feet abruptly.

"Stay here!" he snapped.

His immediate thought was of a posse, and then he saw Kerb Perrin. He had seen Perrin many times, although Perrin had never met him. Slowly, he moved up to the door, uncertain of his course. These were Ben's men, but Ben had always told him that none of them was aware that he owned this ranch or that Voyle was his brother.

"Howdy!" Voyle said. "What can I do for you?"

Kerb Perrin swung down from his horse. Monson, Ducrow and Kiefer were getting down.

"You can make as little trouble as you know how," Perrin said, his eyes gleaming. "All you got to do is stay out of the way. Where's the girls? We want them, and we want your cattle."

"What is this?" Voyle demanded. He wasn't wearing a gun; it was hanging from a clothes-tree in the next room. "You men can't get away with anything here!"

Perrin's face was ugly as he strode toward the door. "That's what *you* think!" he sneered.

The tall old man blocked his way, and Perrin shoved him aside. Perrin had seen the startled faces of the girls inside and knew the men behind him were spreading out.

Ragan swung suddenly and his fist struck Perrin in the mouth. The gunman staggered, his face went white with fury.

A Mexican started from the corral toward the house and Ducrow wheeled, firing from the hip. The man cried out and sprawled over on the hardpacked earth, moaning out his agony.

Perrin had drawn back slowly, his face ugly with rage, a slow trickling of blood from his lips. "For that, I'll kill you!" he snarled at Ragan.

"Not yet, Perrin!"

The voice had a cold ring of challenge, and Kerb Perrin went numb with shock. He turned slowly, to see Mike Bastian standing at the corner of the corral.

Kerb Perrin was profoundly shocked. He had left Bastian a prisoner at Toadstool Canyon. Since he was free now, it could mean that Ben Curry was back in the saddle. It could mean a lot of things. An idean came to kill Mike Bastian, and kill him now!

"You men have made fools of yourselves!" Bastian's

voice was harsh. He stood there in his gray buckskins, his feet a little apart, his black hair rippled by the wind. "Ben Curry's not through! And this place is under his protection. He sent me to stop you, and stop you I shall! Now, any of you who don't want to fight Ben Curry, get out while the getting is good!"

"Stay where you are!" Perrin snapped. "I'll settle with you, Bastian, right now!"

His hand darted down in the sweeping, lightning-fast draw for which he was noted. His lips curled in sneering contempt. Yet, as his gun lifted, he saw flame blossom from a gun in Bastian's hand and a hard object slugged him. Perplexed and disturbed, he took a step backward. Whatever had hit him had knocked his gun out of line. He turned it toward Bastian again. The gun in Mike's hand blasted a second time, and a third.

Perrin could not seem to get his own gun leveled. His mind wouldn't function right, and he felt a strangeness in the stomach. His legs— Suddenly he was on his knees. He tried to get up and saw a dark pool forming near his knees. He must have slipped, he must have— That was blood.

It was his blood!

From far off he heard shouts, then a scream, then the pound of horses' hoofs. Then the thunder of those hoofs seemed to sweep through his brain and he was lying face down in the dirt. And then he knew: Mike Bastian had shot him three times. Mike Bastian had killed him!

He started to scream a protest—and then he just laid there on his face, his cheek against the bloody ground, his mouth half open.

Kerb Perrin was dead.

In that instant that Perrin had reached for his gun, Ducrow suddenly cut and ran toward the corner of the house. Kiefer, seeing his leader gunned down then, made a wild grab for his own weapon. The old man in the door-way killed him with a hastily caught-up rifle.

The others broke for their horses. Mike rushed after them and got off one more shot as they raced out of the yard. It was then he heard the scream, and whirled.

Ducrow had acted with suddenness. He had come to the ranch for women, and women he intended to have. Even as Bastian was killing Perrin, he had rushed for the house. Darting around the corner where two saddle horses were waiting, he was just in time to see Juliana, horrified at the killing, run back into her bedroom. The bedroom window opened beside Ducrow, and the outlaw reached through and grabbed her.

Julie went numb with horror. Ducrow threw her across Perrin's saddle, and with a piggin string, which he always carried from his days as a cowhand, he jerked her ankles together under the horse's belly.

Instantly, he was astride the other horse. Julie screamed, then. Wheeling, he struck her across the mouth with a backhand blow. He caught up the bridle of her horse, drove in spurs to his own mount, and they went out of the ranch yard at a dead run.

Mike hesitated only an instant when he heard Julie scream, then ran for the corner of the house. By the time he round-ed the corner, gun in hand, the two horses were streaking into the pinons. In the dust, he could only catch a glimpse of the riders. He turned and walked back.

That had been a woman's scream, but Dru was in the doorway and he had seen her. Only then did he recall Julie. He sprinted for the doorway.

"Where's Julie?" he shouted to Drusilla. "Look through the house!"

He glanced around quickly. Kerb Perrin, mouth agape, lay dead on the hard earth of the ranch yard. Kiefer lay near the body of the Mexican Ducrow had killed. The whole raid had been a matter of no more than two or three minutes.

Voyle Ragan dashed from the house. "Julie's gone!" he yelled hoarsely. "I'll get a horse!"

Bastian caught his arm. His own dark face was tense and his eyes wide.

"You'll stay here!" he said harshly. "Take care of the woman and the ranch. I'll go after Julie."

Dru ran from the house. "She's gone, Mike, she's gone! They have her!"

Mike walked rapidly to his horse, thumbing shells into his gun. Dru Ragan started to mount another horse.

"You go back to the house!" he ordered.

Dru's chin can up. In that moment she remided him of Ben Curry.

"She's my sister!" Dru cried. "When we find her, she may need a woman's care!"

"All right," Mike said, "but you'll have to do some riding!"

He wheeled the big bay around. The horse Dru had mounted was one of Ben Curry's beautiful horses, bred not only for speed but for staying power.

Mike's mind leaped ahead. Would Ducrow get back with the rest of them? Would he join Monson and Clatt? If he did, it was going to be a problem. Ducrow was a handy man with a six-gun, but the three of them, or more if they were all together, would be nothing less than suicide.

He held the bay horse's pace down. He had taken a swift glance at the hoofmarks of the horses he was trailing, and knew them both.

Would Drew head back for Toadstool Canyon? Bastian considered that as he rode, and decided he would not. Ducrow did not know that Julie was Ben Curry's daughter. But from what Mike had said, Ducrow had cause to believe that Ben was back in the saddle again. And men who went off on rebel raids were not lightly handled by Curry.

Besides, he would want, if possible to keep the girl for himself.

Mike had been taught by Roundy that there was more to trailing a man than following his tracks, for you trailed him down the devious paths of mind as well. He tried to put himself in Ducrow's place.

The man could not have much food, yet on his many outlaw forays he must have learned the country and would know where there was water. Also, there were many ranch hangouts of the outlaws that Ducrow would know. He would probably go to one of them. Remembering the maps that Ben Curry had shown him and made him study, Mike knew the locations of all those places.

The trail turned suddenly off through the chaparral, and Mike turned to follow. Drusilla had said nothing since they started. Once he had glanced at her. Even now, with her face dusty and tear-streaked, she was lovely. Her eyes were fastened on the trail, and he noted with a little thrill of satisfaction that she had brough her rifle along.

Dru certainly was her father's daughter, and the fit companion for any man.

Bastian turned his attention to the trail. Despite the small lead he had, Ducrow had vanished. That taught Mike something of the nature of the man he was tracing; his years of outlawry had taught him how to disappear when need be. The method was simple. Turning off into the thicker desert growth, he had ridden down into a sandy wash.

Here, due to the deep sand and the tracks of horses and cattle, it was a problem and it took Mike several minutes to decide whether Ducrow had gone up or down the wash. Then he caught a hoofprint, and they were off, winding up the sandy wash. Yet Mike knew they would not be in that sand for long. Ducrow would wish to save his horses' strength.

True enough, the trail soon turned out. From then on, it was a nightmare. Ducrow ran off in a straitway, then turned at right angles, weave about in the sandy desert. Several times he had stopped to brush out portions of his trail, bur Roundy had not spent years of training in vain and Mike Bastian hung to the trail like a bloodhound.

Dru, riding behind him, saw him get off and walk, saw him pick up sign where she could see nothing.

Hours passed and the day slowly drew toward an end. Dru, her face pale, realized night would come before they found her sister. She was about to speak, when Mike looked up at her.

"You wanted to come," he said, "so you'll have to take the consequences. I'm not stopping because of the darkness."

"How can you trail them?"

"I can't," he shrugged. "But I think I know where they are going. We'll take a chance."

Darkness closed around them. Mike's shirt stuck to his body with sweat, and a chill wind of the higher plateaus blew down through the trees. He rode on, his face grim and his body weary with long hours in the saddle. The big bay kept on, seemingly unhurt by the long hours of riding. Time and again he patted the big horse, and Dru could hear him talking to it in a low voice. Suddenly at the edge of a clearing, he reined in.

"Dru," he said, "there's a ranch ahead. It's an outlaw hangout. There may be one or more men there. Ducrow may be there. I am going up to find out."

"I'll come too," the girl said impulsively.

"You'll stay here!" His voice was flat. "When I whistle, then you come. Bring my horse along."

He swung down and, slipping off his boots, pulled on his moccasins. Then he went forward into the darkness. Alone, she watched him vanish toward the dark bulk of the buildings. Suddenly a light came on—too soon for him to have arrived.

Mike weaved his way through sage and mesquite to the corral, and worked his way along the bars. Horses were there but it was too dark to make them out. One of them stood near, and he put his hand through the bars, touching the horse's flank. It was damp with sweat.

His face tightened.

The horse stepped away, snorting. As if waiting for just that sound, a light went on in the house: a lamp had been lighted. By that time Mike was at the side of the house, flattened against the wall peering in.

He saw a heavy, square-faced man with a pistol in his hand. The man put the gun under a towel on the table, then began pacing around the room, waiting. Mike smiled grimly, walked around the house and stepped up on the porch. In his moccasins, he made no sound. He opened the door suddenly and stepped into the room.

IX

Obviously the man had been waiting for the sound of boots, of horses, or the jingle of spurs. Even a knock. Mike Bastian's sudden appearance startled him, and he straightened up from the table, his hand near the towel that covered the gun.

Bastian closed the door behind him. The man stared at the black-haired young man who faced him, stared with puckered brow. This man didn't lool like a sheriff to him. Not those tied down guns, or that gray buckskin stained with travel, and no hat.

"You're Walt Sutton," Mike snapped. "Get your hands off that table before I blow you wide open! Get 'em off!"

He jammed the muzzle of the gun into Sutton's stomach with such force that it doubled the man up.

Then he swept the towel from the gun.

"You fool!" he said sharply. "If you'd tried that, I'd have killed you!"

Sutton staggered back, his face gray. He had never even seen Mike's hand move.

"Who are you?" he gasped, struggling to get his wind back.

"I'm Mike Bastian, Ben Curry's foster son. He owns this ranch. He set you up here, gave you stock to get started with, now you double-cross him! Where's Ducrow?"

Sutton swallowed. "I ain't seen him!" he protested.

"You're a liar, Sutton! His horses are out in that corral. I could pistol-whip you, but I'm not going to. You're going to tell me where he is, and now, or I'm going to start shooting!"

Walt Sutton was unhappy. He knew Ducrow as one of Ben Curry's men who had come here before for fresh horses. He had never seen this man who called himself Mike Bastian, yet so far as he knew, no one but Curry himself had ever known the true facts about his ranch. If this man was lying, how could he know?

"Listen, mister," he protested, "I don't want no trouble—least of all with old Ben. He did set me up here. Sure, I seen Ducrow, but he told me the law was after him."

"Do I look like the law?" Mike snapped. "He's kidnapped the daughter of a friend of Curry's, niece of Voyle Ragan. I've got to find him."

"Kipnapped Voyle's niece? Gosh, mister, I wondered why he wanted two saddle horses!"

Mike whistled sharply. "Where'd he go?" he demanded then.

"Darned if I know," Sutton answered. "He came in here maybe an hour ago, wanted two saddle horses and a pack horse loaded with grub. He took two canteens, then, and lit out."

Drusilla appeared in the doorway, and Walt Sutton's eyes

238

went to her.

"I know you," he said. "You're one of Voyle Ragan nieces."

"She is," Mike said "Ducrow kidnapped the other one. I'm going to find him. Get us some grub, but fast!"

Mike paced restlessly while Sutton filled a pack and strapped it behind the saddle of one of the fresh horses he furnished them. The horses were some of those left at the ranch by Ben Curry's orders, and were good.

"No pack horses," Mike had said. "We're travelling fast."

Now, he turned to Sutton again. "You got any idea where Ducrow might be going?"

"Well" — Sutton licked his lips — "he'd kill me if he knew I said anything, but he did say something about Peach Meadow Canyon."

"Peach Meadow?" Bastian stared at Sutton. The canyon was almost a legend in Coconino country. "What did he ask you?"

"If I knowed the trail in there, an' if it was passable."

"What did you say?"

Sutton shrugged. "Well, I've heard tell of that there canyon ever since I been in this country, an' ain't seen no part of it. I've looked, all right. Who wouldn't look, if all they say is true?"

When they were about to mount their horses, Mike turned to the girl and put his hand under her arm.

"Dru," he said, "It's going to be rough, so if you want to go back, say so."

"I wouldn't think of it!" she said firmly.

"Well, I won't say I'm sorry, because I'm not. I'll sure like having you beside me. In fact"—he hesitated, then went on—"it will be nice having you."

That was not what he had started to say, and Dru knew it. She looked at Mike for a moment, her eyes soft. He

239

was tired now, and she could see how drawn his face was. She knew only a little of the ride he had made to reach them before Perrin's outlaws came.

When they were in the saddle, Mike explained a little of what he had in mind. "I doubt Ducrow will stop for anything now," he said. "There isn't a good hiding place within miles, so he'll head right for the canyon country. He may actually know something about Peach Meadow Canyon. If he does, he knows a perfect hideaway. Outlaws often stumble across places in their getaways that a man couldn't find if he looked for it for years."

"What is Peach Meadow Canyon?" Dru asked.

"It's supposed to be over near the river in one of the deep canyons that branch off from the Colorado. According to the story, a fellow found the place years ago, but the Spanish had been there before him, and the Indians before them. There are said to be old Indian ruins in the place, but no way to get into it from the plateau. The Indians found a way through some caves in the Coconino sandstone, and the Spanish are suppposed to have reached it by boat."

"Anyway," he continued, "this prospector who found it said the climate was tropical, or almost. That it was in a branch canyon, that there was fresh water and a nice meadow. Somebody had planted some fruit trees, and when he went back he took a lot of peach pits and was supposed to have planted an orchard.

"Nobody ever saw him or it again," Mike went on, "so the place exists only on his say-so. Ithe Indians alive now swear they have never heard of it. Ducrow might be trying to throw us off, or he might honestly know something."

For several miles the trail was a simple thing. They were riding down the floor of a high-walled canyon from which there was no escape. Nevertheless, from time to time Bastian stopped and examined the sandy floor with matches. Always the tracks were there, and going straight down the anyon.

This was new country to Mike. He knew the altitude was gradually lessening, and believed they would soon emerge on the desert plateau that ran toward the canyon and finally lost itself on the edge of the pine forest.

When they had traveled about seven miles, the canyon ended abruptly and they emerged in a long valley. Mike reined in and swung down.

"Like it or not," he said, "here's where we stop. We can't have a fire, because from here it could be seen for miles. We don't want Ducrow to believe we stopped."

Mike spread his poncho on the sand and handed Dru a blanket. She was feeling the chill and gathered it close around her.

"Aren't you cold?" she said suddenly. "If we sat close together, we could share the blanket."

He hesitated, then sat down alongside her and pulled the blanket across his shoulders, grateful for the warmth. Leaning back against the rock, warmed by proximity and the blanket, they dozed a little.

Mike had loosened his girths and ground-hitched the horses. He wasn't worried about them straying off.

When the sky was just faintly gray, he opened his eyes. Dru's head was on his shoulder and she was sleeping. He could feel the rise and fall of her breathing against his body. He glanced down at her face, amazed that this could happen to him—that he, Mike Bastian, foster son of an outlaw, could be sitting alone in the desert with this girl sleeping on his shoulder!

Some movement of his must have awakened her, for her breath caught, and then she looked up. He could see the sleepy smile in her eyes and on her mouth.

"I was tired!" She whispered the words, and made no effort to move her head from his shoulder. "You've nice shoulders," she said. "If we were riding anywhere else, I'd not want to move at all."

241

"Nor I." He glanced at the stars. "We'd better get up. I think we can chance a very small fire and a quick cup of coffee."

While he was breaking dried mesquite and greasewood, Dru got the pack open and dug out the coffee and some bread. There was no time for anything else.

The fire made but little light, shielded by the rocks and kept very small, and there was less glow now due to the grayness of the sky. They ate quickly.

When they were in the saddle again, he turned down the trail left by the two saddle horses and the pack horse he was following. Sign was dim, but could be followed without dismounting. Dawn broke, and the sky turned red and gold, then blue. The sun lifted and began to take some of the chill from their muscles.

The trail crossed the valley, skirting an alkali lake, and then dipped into the rocky wilderness that preceded the pine forest. He could find no signs of a camp. Julie, who lacked the fire and also the strength of Dru, must be almost dead with weariness, for Ducrow was not stopping. Certainly, the man had more than a possible destination before him. In fact, the farther they rode, the more confident Mike was that the outlaw knew exactly where he was headed.

The pines closed around them and the trail became more difficult to follow. It was slow going, and much of it Mike Bastian walked. Suddenly he stopped, scowling.

The trail, faint as it had been, had vanished into thin air!

"Stay where you are," he told Dru "I've got to look around a bit."

Mike studied the ground carefully. Then he walked back to the last tracks he had seen. Their own tracks did not cover them, as he had avoided riding over them in case he needed to examine the hoofprints once more.

Slowly, Mike paced back and forth over the pine needles. Then he stopped and studied the surrounding timber very carefully. It seemed to be absolutely uniform in appearance. Avoiding the trail ahead, he left the girl and circled into the woods, describing a slow circle around the horses.

There were no tracks.

He stopped, his brow furrowed. It was impossible to lose them after following so far—yet they were gone, and they had left no trail. He walked back to the horses again, and Dru stared at him, her eyes wide.

"Wait a minute," he said as she began to speak. "I want to think."

He studied, inch by inch, the woods on his left, the trail ahead, and then the trail on his right. Nothing offered a clue. The tracks of three horses had simply vanished as though the animals and their riders had been swallowed into space.

On the left the pines stood thick, and back inside the woods the brush was so dense as to allow no means of passing through it. That was out, then. He had studied that brush and had walked through those woods, and if a horseman did turn that way there would be no place to go.

The trail ahead was trackless, so it had to be on the right. Mike truned and walked again to the woods on his right. He inched over the ground, yet there was nothing, no track, no indication that anything heavier than a rabbit had passed that way. It was impossible, yet it happened.

"Could they have backtracked?" Dru asked suddenly. "Over the same trail?"

Mike shook his head. "There were no tracks," he said, "but those going ahead, I think—I'm a fool! A darned fool!" He grinned at her. "Lend me your hat."

Puzzled, she removed her sombrero and handed it to him. He turned and using the hat for a fan, began to wave it over the ground to let the wind disturb the surface needles. Patiently, he worked over the area around the last tracks seen, and then to the woods on both sides of the trail. Suddenly, he stopped.

"Got it!" he said. "Here they are!"

Dru ran to him. He pointed to a track, then several more.

"Ducrow was smart," Mike explained. "He turned at right angles and rode across the open space, and then turned back down the way he had come, riding over on the far side. Then he dismounted and, coming back, gathered pine needles from somewhere back in the brush and came along here, pressing the earth down and scattering the needles to make it seem there had been no traces at all!"

Mounting again, they started back, and from time to time he dismounted to examine the trail. Suddenly the tracks ended and turned off into thick woods. Leading their horses, they followed.

"Move quietly as you can," Mike said softly "We may be close, now. Or he may wait and try to ambush us."

"You think he knows we're following him?" Dru asked.

"Sure! And he knows I'm a tracker. He'll use every trick in the books, now."

For awhile, the trail was not difficult to follow and they rode again. Mike Bastian could not take his mind from the girl who rode with him. What would she think when she discovered her father was an outlaw? That he was the mysterious leader of the outlaws?

X

Pine trees thinned out, and before them was the vast blue and misty distance of the canyon. Mike slid to the ground and walked slowly forward on mocassined feet. There were pines and the cracked and splintered rim of the canyon, breaking sharply off to fall away into the vast depths. Carefully, he scouted the edge of the canyon, and when he saw the trail he stopped flat-footed and stared, his heart in his mouth.

Had they gone down *there?* He knelt on the rock. Yes, there was the scar of a horse's hoof. He walked out a little farther, looking down.

The cliff fell away for hundreds of feet without even a hump in the wall, then just a little farther along was the trial. It was a rocky ledge scarcely three feet wide that ran steeply down the side of the rock from the canyon's rim. On the left the wall, on the right the vast, astonishing emptiness of the canyon.

Thoughtfully, he walked back and explained.

"All right, Mike," Dru nodded. "if you're ready, I am."

He hesitated to bring the horses, but decided it would be the best thing. He drew his rifle from the saddle scabbard and jacked a shell into the chamber.

Dru looked at him, steady-eyed. "Mike, maybe he'll be waiting for us," she said. "We may get shot. Especially you."

Bastian nodded. "That could be," he agreed.

She came toward him. "Mike, who are you, what are you? Uncle Voyle seemed to know you, or about you, and that outlaw, Perrin. He knew you. Then I heard you say Ben Curry had sent you to stop them from raiding the ranch. Are you an outlaw, Mike?"

For as long as a man might have counted a slow ten, Mike stared out over the canyon, trying to make up his mind. Now at this stage, there was only one thing he could say.

"No, Dru, not exactly, but I was raised by an outlaw," he explained. "Ben Curry brought me up like his own son, with the idea that I would take over the gang when he stepped out."

"You lived with them in their hideout?"

"When I wasn't out in the woods." He nodded. "Ben Curry had me taught everything—how to shoot, to track, to ride, even to open safes and locks."

"What's he like, this Ben Curry?" Dru asked.

"He's quite a man!" Mike Bastian said, smiling. "When he started outlawing, everybody was rustling a few cows, and he just went a step further and robbed banks and stages, or planned the robberies and directed them. I don't expect he really figured himself bad. He might have done a lot of other things, for he has brains. But he killed a man—and then in getting away, he killed another. The first one was justified. The second one— Well, he was in a hurry."

"Are you apologizing for him?" Dru said quickly. "After all, he was an outlaw and a killer."

He glanced at her. "He was, yes. And I am not making any apologies for him, nor would he want them. He's a man who always stood on his own two feet. Maybe he was wrong, buy there were the circumstances. And he was mighty good to me. I didn't have a home, no place to go, and he took me in and treated me right."

"Was he a big man, Mike? A big old man?"

He did not look at her. She knew, then?

"In many ways," he said, "he is one of the biggest men I know. We'e better get started."

It was like stepping off into space, yet the horses took it calmly enough. They were mountain bred and would go anywhere as long as they could get a foothold on something.

The red maw of the canyon gaped to receive them and they went down, following the narrow, switchback trail that seemed to be leading them into the very center of the earth.

It was late afternoon before they started down, and nown the shadows began to creep up the canyon walls, reaching with ghostly fingers for the vanished sunlight. Overhead the red blazed with the setting sun's reflection and seemed to be hurling arrows of flame back into the sky. The depths of the canyon seemed to chill after the sun on the plateau, and Mike walked warily, always a little ahead of the horse he was leading.

Dru was riding, and when he glanced back once, she smiled brightly at him, keep her eyes averted from the awful depths below.

Mike had no flair for making love, for his knowledge of women was slight. He wished know that he knew more of their ways, knew the things to say that would appeal to a girl.

A long time later they reached the bottom, and far away on their right they could hear the river rushing through the canyon. Mike knelt, and striking a match, he studied the trail. The tracks turned back into a long canyon that led back from the river.

He got into the saddle then, his rifle across his saddle, and rode forward.

At the end, it was simple. The long chase had led to a quiet meadow, and he could smell the grass before he reached it, could hear the babble of a small stream. The canyon walls flared wide and he saw, not far away, the faint sparkle of a fire.

Dru came alongside him. "Is . . . that them?" she asked, low-voiced.

"It couldn't be anyone else." Her hand was on his arm and he put his own hand over it. "I've got to go up there alone, Dru. I'll have to kill him, you know."

"Yes, she said, simply, "but don't *you* be killed!"

He started to ride forward and she caught his arm.

"Mike, why have you done all this?" she asked. "She isn't your sister."

"No." He looked very serious in the vague light. "She's yours."

He turned his head and spoke to the horse. The animal started forward.

When, shortly, he stopped the mount, he heard a sound nearby. Dru Ragan was close behind him.

"Dru," he whispered, "you've *got* to stay back! Hold my horse. I'm going up on foot."

He left her like that and walked steadily forward. Even before he got to the fire, he could see them. The girl, her

247

head slumped over her arms, half dead with weariness, and Ducrow bending over the fire. From time to time Ducrow glanced at the girl. Finally, he reached over and cuffed her on the head.

"Come on, get some of this coffee into you!" he growled.

"This is where we stay—in Peach Meadow Canyon. Might as well give up seein' that sister of yours, because you're my woman, now." He sneered. "Monson and them, they ran like scared foxes! No bottom to them. I come for a woman, and I got one!"

"Why don't you let me go?" Juliana protested. "My father will pay you well. He has lots of money."

"Your pa?" Ducrow stared at her. "I thought Voyle Ragan was your uncle?"

"He is. I mean Ben Ragan. He ranches up north of the canyon."

"North of the canyon?" Ducrow laughed "Not unless he's a Mormon, he don't. What's he look like, this pa of yours?"

"He's a great big man, with iron-gray hair, a heavy jaw—" She stopped, staring at Ducrow. "What's the matter with you?"

Ducrow got slowly to his feet. "Your Pa—Ben Ragan? A big man with gray hair, an' maybe a scar on his jaw— that him?"

"Oh yes! Take me to him! He'll pay you well!"

Suddenly, Ducrow let out a guffaw of laughter. He slapped his leg and bellowed. "Man, oh, man! Is that a good one! You're Ben Curry's daughter! Why that old—" He sobered. "What did you call him? Ragan? Why, honey, that old man of yours is the biggest outlaw in the world! Or was until today! Well, of all the—"

"You've laughed enough, Ducrow!"

As Mike Bastian spoke, he stepped to the edge of the

firelight. "You leave a tough trail, but I followed it."

Ducrow turned, half crouching, his cruel eyes glaring at Bastian.

"Roundy was right," he snarled. "You could track a snake across a flat rock! Well, now that you're here, what are you goin' to do?"

"That depends on you, Ducrow. You can drop your gun and I'll take you in for a trial. Or you can shoot it out."

"Drop my guns?" Ducrow chuckled. "You'd actually take me in, too! You're too soft, Bastian. You'd never make the boss man old Ben Curry was. He would never even of said yes, or no, he would have seen me and gone to blastin'! You got a sight to learn, youngster. Too bad you ain't goin' to live long enough to learn it."

Ducrow lifted one hand carelessly and wiped it across the tobacco-stained stubble of his beard. His right hand swept down for his gun even as his left touched his face. His gun came up, spouting flame.

Mike Bastian palmed his gun and momentarily held it rigid, then he fired.

Ducrow winced like he had been slugged in the chest, and then he lifted on his tiptoes. His gun came level again.

"You're . . .fast!" he gasped. "Devilish fast!"

He fired, and then Mike triggered his gun once more. The second shot spun Ducrow around and he fell, face down at the edge of the fire.

Dru came running, her rifle in her hand, but when she saw Mike still standing, she dropped the rifle and ran to him.

"Oh, Mike!" she sobbed. "I was so frightened! I though you were killed!"

Julie started to rise, then fell headlong into a faint. Dru rushed to her side.

Mike Bastian absently thumbed shells into his gun and stared down at the fallen man. He had killed a third man.

Suddenly, and profoundly, he wished with all his heart he would never have to kill another.

He holstered his weapon, and gathered up the dead man carried him away from the fire. He would bury him here in Peach Meadow Canyon.

XI

Sunlight lay upon the empty street of the settlement in Toadstool Canyon when Mike Bastian, his rifle crosswise on his saddle, rode slowly into the lower end of the town.

Beside him, sitting straight in her saddle, rode Dru Ragan. Julie had stayed at the ranch, but Dru flatly refused. Ben Curry was her father, and she was going to him outlaw camp or not.

If Dave Lenaker had arrived, Mike thought, he was quiet enough, for there was no sound. No horses stood at the hitch-rails, and the door of the saloon stood wide open.

Something fluttered on the ground and Mike looked at it quickly. It was a torn bit of cloth on a man's body. The man was a stranger. Dru noticed it, and her face paled.

His rifle at ready, Mike rode on, eyes shifting from side to side. A man's wrist lay in sight across a window sill his pistol on the porch outside. There was blood on the stoop of another house.

"There's been a fight," Mike said, "and a bad one. You'd better get set for the worst."

Dru said nothing, but her mouth held firm. At the last building, the mess hall, a man lay dead in a doorway. They rode on, then drew up at the foot of the stone steps and dismounted. Mike shoved his rifle back in the saddle scabbard and loosened his six-guns.

"Let's go!" he said.

The wide veranda was empty and still, but when he stepped into the huge living room, he stopped in amazement. five men sat about a table playing cards.

Ben Curry's head came up and he waved at them.

"Come on in, Mike!" he called. "Who's that with you? Dru, by all that's holy!"

Doc Sawyer, Roundy, Garlin and Colley were there. Garlin's head was bandaged, and Colley had one foot stretched out stiff and straight, as did Ben Curry. But all were smiling.

Dru ran to her father and fell on her knees beside him. "Oh, Dad!" she cried. "We were so scared!"

"What happened here?" Mike demanded. "Don't sit there grinning! Did Dave Lenaker come?"

"He sure did, and what do you think?" Doc said. "It was Rigger Molina got him! Rigger got to Weaver and found out Perrin had double-crossed him before he ever pulled the job. He discovered that Perrin had lied about the guards, so he rushed back. When he found out that Ben was crippled, and that Kerb Perrin had run out, he waited for Lenaker himself.

"He was wonderful, Mike," Doc continued. "I never saw anything like it! He paced the veranda out there like a bear in a cage, swearing and waiting for Lenaker. Muttered, 'Leave you in the lurch, will they? I'll show 'em! Lenaker thinks he can gun you down because you're gettin' old, does he? Well, killer I may be, but I can kill him!' And he did, Mike. They shot it out in the street down there. Dave Lenaker, as slim and tall as you, and that great bear of a Molina.

"Lenaker beat him to the draw," Doc went on. "He got two bullets into the Rigger, but Molina wouldn't go down. He stood there spraddle-legged in the street and shot until both guns were empty. Lenaker kept shooting, and must have hit Molina five times, but when he went down, Rigger walked over to him and spat in his face. 'That for double-crossers!' he said. He was magnificent!"

"They fooled me, Mike," Roundy said. "I seen trouble a-comin' an' figured I'd better get to old Ben. I never

251

figured they'd slip in behind you, like they done. Then the news of Lenaker comin' got me. I knowed him an' was afraid of him, so I figured to save Ben Curry I'd get down the road and drygulch him. Never killed a white man in my life, Mike, but I was sure aimin' to! But he got by me on another trail. After Molina killed Lenaker, his boys and some of them from here started after the gold they'd figured was in this house."

"Doc here," Garlin said, "is some fighter! I didn't know he had it in him."

"Roundy, Doc, Garlin an' me," Colley said, "we sided Ben Curry. It was a swell scrap while it lasted. Garlin got one through his scalp, and I got two bullets in the leg. Aside from that, we came out all right."

Briefly, then, Mike explained all that transpired, how he had killed Perrin, and then had trailed Ducrow to Peach Meadow Canyon and the fight there.

"Where's the gang?" he demanded now. "All gone?"

"All the live ones." Ben Curry nodded grimly. "There's a few won't go anywhere. Funny, the only man who ever fooled he was Rigger Molina. I never knew the man was that loyal, yet he stood by me when I was in no shape to fight Lenaker. Took that fight right off my hands. He soaked up lead like a sponge soaks water!"

Ben Curry looked quickly at Dru. "So you know you're the daughter of an outlaw? Well, I'm sorry, Dru. I never aimed for you to know. I was gettin' shet of this business, and planned to settle down on a ranch with your mother and live out the rest of my days plumb peaceful."

"Why don't you?" Dru demanded.

He looked up at her, his admiring eyes taking in her slim, well-rounded figure. "You reckon she'll have me?" he asked. "She looked a sight like you when she was younger, Dru."

"Of course, she'll have you! She doesn't know—or didn't

252

know until Julie told her. But I think she guessed. *I* knew. I saw you talking with some men once, and later heard they were outlaws, and then I began hearing about Ben Curry."

Curry looked thoughtfully from Dru to Mike.

"Is there something between you two? Or am I an old fool?"

Mike flushed, and kept his eyes away from Dru.

"He's a fine man, Dru," Doc Sawyer said. "And well educated, if I do say so—who taught him all he knows."

"All he knows!" Roundy stared at Doc with comtempt. "Book learnin'! Where would that gal be but for what I told him? How to read sign, how to foller a trail? Where would she be?"

Mike took Dru out to the veranda then.

"I can read sign, all right," he said, "but I'm no hand at reading the trail to a woman's heart. You would have to help me, Dru."

She laughed softly, and her eyes were bright as she slipped her arm through his. "Why, Mike, you've been blazing a trail over and back and up again, ever since I met you in the street at Weaver!"

Suddenly, she sobered. "Mike, let's get some cattle and go back to Peach Meadow Canyon. You said you could make a better trail in, and it would be a wonderful place! Just you and I and—"

"Sure," he said, "in Peach Meadow Canyon."

Roundy craned his head toward the door, then he chuckled.

"That youngster," he said, "he may not know all the trails, but he sure gets where he's goin', he sure does!"

FINE WORKS OF FICTION AND NON-FICTION AVAILABLE FROM CARROLL & GRAF

☐ Brown, Harry/A WALK IN THE SUN $3.95
☐ De Quincey, Thomas/CONFESSIONS OF AN ENGLISH OPIUM EATER AND OTHER WRITINGS $4.95
☐ Farrell, J.G./THE SIEGE OF KRISHNAPUR $4.95
☐ Higgins, George V./A CHOICE OF ENEMIES $3.50
☐ Hilton, James/RANDOM HARVEST $4.50
☐ Huxley, Aldous/GREY EMINENCE $4.95
☐ Innes, Hammond/THE WRECK OF THE MARY DEARE $3.50
☐ Johnson, Josephine/NOW IN NOVEMBER $4.50
☐ O'Hara, John/FROM THE TERRACE $4.95
☐ Proffitt, Nicholas/GARDENS OF STONE $3.95
☐ Purdy, James/CABOT WRIGHT BEGINS $4.50
☐ Rechy, John/BODIES AND SOULS $4.50
☐ Scott, Paul/THE LOVE PAVILION $4.50
☐ Wharton, William/SCUMBLER $3.95

Available at fine bookstores everywhere or use this coupon for ordering:

Carroll & Graf Publishers, Inc., 260 Fifth Avenue, N.Y., N.Y. 10001

Please send me the books I have checked above. I am enclosing $_____ (please add $1.75 per title to cover postage and handling.) Send check or money order—no cash or C.O.D.'s please. N.Y residents please add 8¼% sales tax.

Mr/Mrs/Miss _____

Address _____

City _____ State/Zip _____

Please allow four to six weeks for delivery.